Tha

MW00856449

INVISIBLE

WOUNDS

AN EXIT BUT NO ESCAPE

FAREED S. SALAHUDDIN

Copyright © 2024 by DYS Press LLC

All rights reserved. No part of this book may be reproduced or used in any manner without written permission of the copyright owner except for the use of quotations in a book review.

This is a work of fiction, inspired by true events. Names and characters either are the product of the author's imagination or are used fictitiously unless given permission by the individual. Any resemblance to actual persons, living or dead, events, or locales may be coincidental.

National Child Abuse Coalition

www.nationalchildabusecoalition.org

National Center for Missing & Exploited Children's Cyber

Tipline

Call- 800.843.5678

Text- 800.422.4453

First paperback edition April 2024

DYS Press LLC
San Diego, CA.
619.856.3816

Paperback ISBN: 979-8-218-97637-8

Published by DYS Press LLC

www.fareedsalahuddindyspress.com

DEDICATION

Acknowledging the unwavering support and encouragement I've received, this page is devoted to my cherished circle of family and friends, who have stood by me from childhood to the present moment. Their belief in my potential has been a lighthouse in the journey of bringing this narrative to life. If your name is not listed, don't be upset. I have a big family, and it would take me all day to thank everyone. You have all impacted my life in a way and I thank all of you. Too many cousins, aunts, uncles, in-laws, and grandparents to name.

To my three siblings, I owe a heartfelt thanks; your role in shaping this story cannot be understated. Racqueleona Clyburn, Wanya Salahuddin, and Keanu Salahuddin, I thank you again. I would like to thank my little family Russell Stevenson-Salahuddin, Sebastian Salahuddin, Marci Salahuddin, and Maachi Salahuddin for the constant love and support.

To my mother Dana Salahuddin, you are my world. You have given me the greatest support and motivation. You are always with me in spirit. I love you dearly. To my father Fareed Salahuddin, you have impacted me in a way that I will never forget. You are a man of many talents and I thank you for contribution, it has made a difference in my life.

I must also express my deepest appreciation to Sheila Conroy, a paragon of clinical therapy, whose dedication to her profession has profoundly impacted my life. Sheila's enduring positivity and her unwavering commitment to assist those in need have not only influenced my path but have also been a source of inspiration and strength. To Sheila, whose passion for her vocation has altered many destinies, I extend my deepest gratitude. Your work resonates in the lives you've uplifted and within the essence of this tale.

CONTENTS

Chapter 1

POISON IN MY DNA

To know a man, you need to know his parents.

Unless you are an orphan (and sometimes even if you are), much of the person you become is either influenced by or affected by those who gave birth to you and raised you. Some people grow up to be exactly like their folks. Young men become carbon copies of their fathers—down to the way they clear their throats and rely on their spouses to knot their ties.

Other people are so repelled by the behavior of their caregivers that they sprint in the opposite direction. Growing girls exhausted by the domestic docility of their mothers throw themselves into rigorous university studies or high-powered careers.

If you're introspective, you'll try to take on the good parts of your parents while leaving the bad behind. Unfortunately, *leaving the bad behind* isn't as easy as many might think. It is not merely looking at your father's bad temper or your mother's hoarder tendencies and deciding, *"Nope, not for me!"*

The thing about a bad trait is that it often works like a sleeper agent. Weaving its way through your conscious mind undetected and embedding itself into your character until the *exact right* circumstances push you over the edge. Then, suddenly, you're smashing furniture in a blind rage and stashing away the wood chips in a storage box afterward just in case they might someday be useful.

To discard a bad trait, you have to do the work of truly understanding it. You need to figure out where it comes from, what triggers it, and how it manifests. You need to be intricately aware of the details so that you do not accidentally overlook them. You need to know what poisons your parents gave you when they blessed you with their DNA. And then you need to know those poisons intimately.

The thing is, though, that good traits and bad traits are rarely equally distributed between parents. Maybe your mom was a saint, and your dad was a devil, or vice-versa. Maybe your folks were both bad in some ways and good in others.

My dad gave me a hell of a lot more poison than my mom.

Let's put it this way: if Mom was a mild exposure to mercury, then Dad was a value-sized bottle of Anthrax.

And yet, I've found that it does me no good to pretend like Dad was more monster than man. As much as he hurt me, I still try my best to remember that he was a human being all the same. Furthermore, he was my *dad.* And for better or worse, he had an enormous effect on the person that I am today.

Dad was born in California.

A child of the Sunshine State, Dad was predictably gregarious, outgoing, and magnetic. He was short, muscular, and handsome, and paid a good deal of attention to his hair. For a period of time, he had an afro. Then, he had braids. Finally, he chopped his hair short—and kept it that way. Dad would always keep a tube of Carmex lip balm on him. I would soon emulate that decorum, we couldn't go anywhere without it.

Even though he could be fun and goofy, his face while resting was serious.

Most people who didn't know him probably thought that he was mean. But then, you'd get to talking with him, and he'd crack a joke or laugh freely at yours—and you'd realize that he wasn't such an unapproachable guy after all.

Dad was also a hard worker. One of the hardest workers that I have ever known. He drove trucks for a shipping company and was often on the road for weeks at a time. He provided for his family and took pride in doing so.

My uncle would always tell me how much my dad loved all of us. Although, he didn't have to remind me. I knew.

Despite his socially easygoing nature, Dad could be very protective. You couldn't say something slick to my dad without having to answer for it. Because Dad didn't let anyone play with him, he could command respect.

Like most boys, I looked up to my dad. The guy was my protector. My hero. There was a time in my life in which I hoped to be just like him—poison and all.

Retrospectively, however, I find speaking about my father in this manner to be a confusing task. You see, in my mind, there are two versions of my dad. One version is the man that I have just described to you. The other is a cruel, sadistic, abusive villain. The kind of guy who would beat his own children half-to-death over the slightest infraction. The kind of guy who I would rather die than become.

As I look back on my childhood, it is sometimes hard to reconcile these two versions of the man who raised me.

And yet, I still try anyway.

In the years since my adolescence, I've found myself thinking a lot about the people who raised me. Even though it is useless, I've thoroughly tortured myself with hypotheticals.

Would things have been different if my mother hadn't gotten sick?

Could I have said something earlier on to change my fate? Done something?

But most prominently: *Why did the man who gave me my life try so hard to destroy it?*

One thing that most children of abuse suffer from is the tendency to blame themselves for everything that has gone wrong in their lives. We make countless excuses for our parents. We undulate like fickle pendulums between being fiercely aware that we were faultless children and desperately desiring to repent at the feet of our parents.

I think a lot about my dad's actions. Whether or not I ever did anything to truly warrant the years of torture and pain that he put me through. As an adult who has somewhat since healed and processed my childhood, I know that nothing I could've done would have ever justified the punishments that I received. Being beaten half-to-death. Being starved of food. Being treated like filth and garbage.

I don't know why my dad became the monster that he was. Maybe it was drinking or drugs. Maybe it was some buried-deep trauma that my mom's death summoned to the surface. Maybe it was something else entirely.

My attempts to understand my parents have ranged from therapeutic to agonizing to completely numbing. But I think that it is important to not swallow down the poison quietly. Talking about it, writing about it, and expressing it is my way of coming to terms with it and furthermore understanding it.

I don't know if I'll ever get answers to my questions. I don't know if *understanding* someone is the same as *knowing* them. But I *do* know one thing.

I won't be silent about what happened. Because experience has taught me that even if you are ignored 99 times out of 100—all it takes is for one person to hear you out.

To know a man, you need to know his parents. Then, you need to know his childhood.

So, let me tell you a little bit about mine.

Chapter 2

"I WILL NOT GET SUSPENDED"

*I*t wasn't fair.

That was the thought running through my head as I sat on the wooden bench outside the principal's office.

I had never been a bad kid. Not really. But as with all kids, sometimes things just happened that jumbled up my sense of right and wrong. And when that happened, rational was just another three-syllable word in the dictionary.

Like, for example, this time.

My teacher had been showing us how to make s'mores. The entire ordeal had been going roughly as good as one might expect considering the fact that we were all antsy elementary schoolers dealing with sticky marshmallows and chocolate bars.

But then, one of my classmates dropped her s'more.

For some kids, dropping food on the floor was a nonissue. I have seen classmates who swore by the "five-second rule" pick up everything from Dunkaroos to Fruit Roll-Ups off the floor without hesitation.

However, if you were raised properly, you knew that once something fell to the ground, it was as good as gone. Ant food, if you will.

That must've been what was running through this girl's mind as she stared at her campfire creation sitting in pieces on the hard tile. She started to cry, her shrill little voice drawing the attention of everybody in the room.

One of the boys next to me started giggling at her outburst. I coughed into my palm.

"Who just laughed?" our teacher demanded, whipping around to glare at us.

The other boy was faster to the punch than I was. He pointed at me; his guilty eyes wider than platters.

I tried to insist that he was lying.

Unfortunately, the teacher just shook her head. "You need to learn to take responsibility for yourself, Feisal."

The teacher marched over to me, snatching the s'more I carefully made off my paper plate. "No s'more for you today."

"But, but-," I felt my heart sink into my chest.

I had always wanted to taste a s'more. I had been inundated with cartoon and media depictions of the delicious treat since I was old enough to crane my head up at the TV. And as a result, s'mores had become to me what food and wine was to Tantalus. And irresistible desire—now completely out of reach.

The teacher, noticing my despair, said, "Stop that. You'll gain a lot of character once you learn to own up to the things that you do."

How ironic! I thought, glaring at the boy next to me.

He was still giggling. But this time, he had changed the target of his mockery from the girl to me.

To say that I was furious would have been a massive, massive understatement. In my child-brain, this boy had just ruined what was likely to be the best food experience of my young life. And now he had the nerve to laugh.

Without thinking, I grabbed the Ticonderoga #2 pencil off my desk and stabbed it into his shoe.

Either his shoe was made of cardboard, or I had the sharpest pencil on planet Earth—because the tip of my pencil completely punctured the toe of his sneaker. Both he and I are lucky that I did not pierce his actual foot.

Regardless, that is how I ended up on the bench outside the principal's office. The secretary had just finished up with calling my parents to tell them about the incident and to let them know that I was going to be suspended for seven days, and I was secretly wondering if she would also be so kind as to draft up my will.

When I got home, my mom was waiting for me. Her arms were crossed, and her phone was already in her hand with my dad's number pre-dialed.

"You tell him what you did," Mom said, pushing the phone into my hands.

Hitting call on the phone felt about as damning as pulling the trigger on a gun aimed right at your head.

When Dad answered, I could hear a familiar din coming from his side of the call. Dad was a truck driver. This meant that he was often out on the road for days at a time as a part of his regular work responsibilities.

Mom quietly urged me to put the phone on speaker so that she could listen in to the conversation. I did, feeling red with humiliation.

I beat around the bush for a little bit, trying to put off eventually having to tell Dad the truth. He wasn't having it.

"Son, I'm busy. Get to the point," Dad said.

I took a breath. Then, I told Dad what I'd done, and what the punishment was.

As expected, Dad blew up like a bottle rocket. "Are you serious, Feisal? That's the stupidest thing I've ever heard a boy do. What the Hell were you thinking?"

I tried to stammer out an answer. No luck.

"I swear to god, as soon as I get home, I'm going to smack some sense into you."

I didn't have a chance to say anything. Mom ripped the phone away from my hands. She snapped into the receiver, "Jamal, you must be out of your damn mind if you think you're going to put your hands on my son. Nobody puts their hands on my kids. Do you understand me?"

Dad faltered.

The phrase "don't fight fire with fire" had never really resonated with me. Even though my parents had never been outright cruel to one another, I'd known from a young age that nothing worked better to extinguish my dad's flames than my mom's inferno.

After a moment of contemplation, Dad's voice came over the line again. "Hand me to Feisal, Yvette."

She did.

Dad said, "Alright, son. Go get a pencil and a few pieces of paper." His voice was gruff but mollified. "Sit down at the table and write I will not get suspended one hundred times."

"One hundred?" I wailed. When you are a kid, the difference between one hundred and one hundred thousand is only an extra word.

"Yes. And when I come home next week, I'm going to check it. You better write it one hundred times, Feisal. If you miss even one line, you'll be sorry."

Dad was not the kind of guy you fooled around with. When he said something, it became law. And the words if, and, or, but may as well have been Yiddish—because they certainly did not have a place in the English language.

So, for the next week, I did nothing but write I will not get suspended. And once I'd finished my lines, I triple-checked to ensure that there were exactly one hundred of them.

By the same time the following week, I found myself waiting at the side door for Dad to pull into the driveway. I held the loose-leaf papers with my sentences tightly in my hands, ready to show Dad the work that I had done.

My writing had been impeccably neat. Especially for a kid as young as myself. I wanted to make sure that I did the punishment right.

And who knew? Maybe Dad would be so impressed by my penmanship that he would forget that he was even mad at me altogether.

After about thirty minutes of waiting, Mom came up behind me and tapped my shoulder. "He got another assignment. He's not coming home tonight," she murmured.

This news upset me greatly.

In fact, I was more upset at the fact that I was not going to see my father than I had been while writing my lines.

Mom seemed to sense my distress. She took the paper from my hands and told me that she would give it to Dad when he came back so that he could look at it. She carefully tucked the paper into the kitchen junk drawer for safekeeping.

Yet, as I left the kitchen, I had the sense that the paper would be forgotten about long before Dad finally came home.

And unfortunately, I was right.

Chapter 3

ABSENCE MAKES THE HEART GROW FONDER

Two days after being suspended, Dad came home.

He didn't ask to see my paper. He just trudged to his room, mumbling something about wanting to sleep in a real bed after nearly eighty hours straight on the road.

Part of me almost wanted to show Dad the paper. I had, after all, spent a good deal of time working on it. But the wiser part of me knew that it was best in this case not to poke the bear. Telling my dad about the paper would only remind him about my suspension. And then, he'd probably be in a bad mood for the remainder of his limited time at home.

I didn't want to be the reason he got into a bad mood.

So, I said nothing, and played quietly with my little brother, Wayne, while Dad slept.

This routine was pretty normal in my family. Dad would work for a few days at a time, and we kids would miss the hell out of him. Then, when he finally came home, he'd be too exhausted from his job to give us the time and attention that we were starved for.

It wasn't like Dad didn't love us. He was just tired. We knew that.

Dad loved us a lot. Especially me and my sister, Rhondelle. *Especially* Rhondelle. In his eyes, that little girl could do no wrong. He loved my little brother, too—but for whatever reason, he never built the same relationship with Wayne that he did with Rhondelle and me.

Later that night, Dad woke up.

It was way past dark. Rhondelle was in her room, and Wayne was in his. Both were either asleep or going to be asleep within the hour. But I was in the living room, wide awake.

Dad acknowledged me with a head nod. Then, he grabbed a drink from the kitchen before returning to sit next to me on the couch. I had to crush my smile. Something about sitting on the couch with my dad while my younger siblings were asleep made me feel older. Like a man. Or at least like someone who was going to become one someday.

"You wanna watch a movie, Feisal?" Dad asked, his voice muted.

I nodded eagerly.

Dad nodded toward our clunky brown entertainment center. "Then go get one of the DVDs and pop that sucker in. You can read, right?"

I blinked, hoping that my dad's question was rhetorical. When I saw no sign of humor on his face, I quickly bobbed my head.

"Good. Get the one that says *Player's Club* on it. I'm in the mood for that one."

I obediently hopped off the couch and got the movie. I put the DVD into our player and handed Dad the remote so that he could control the volume.

Dad had a habit of showing me movies that I was far too young to watch. Before I'd even hit the double-digits, I'd seen everything from Eddie Murphy's *Norbit* to Robin Harris' *Bebe's Kids.* Dad swore that the latter was okay because it was a cartoon.

The first movie I ever watched with Dad was a comedy film with Chris Rock in it called *Pootie Tang.* I remember not knowing what the hell I was watching. I grew up not liking pie or jelly because of that movie, because of the scene where Stacey makes Pootie a pie and he rubs it all over his face and chest and she tackles him through a window afterward. I didn't like the movie so much, but Dad thought it was hilarious. So, to make him laugh, I would say the line, "Tippy tow, tippy tay, I'm Pootie Tang!"

He was the only one who thought it was funny. The rest of the adults in my family mostly just shook their heads in mild disappointment.

I didn't mind the polite scorn, though. As long as I could make Dad laugh.

I think one of the reasons I liked these quiet little moments with Dad was because I had so few of them to hang on to. Dad was out of town so often that the number of good memories I have to look back upon with him is sparse.

That isn't to say that there were *no* good times. There were a few. Like, for example, the times that Dad would take me fishing. It would be Dad, his best friend, and me. Or sometimes just Dad and me.

But mostly, my memories of Dad were of me wishing that he'd be home. Wishing that he didn't have a job that took him away from us so often. That didn't leave him so tired whenever he was back in the house.

A lot of my friends had dads that only worked during the day. Some even only worked until dinnertime. I often wondered why that couldn't be *my* dad. Why he'd chosen to be a truck driver of all things—or why being a truck driver had chosen him.

There's that phrase, *absence makes the heart grow fonder.* I don't know if that is true necessarily, but absence sure as hell makes your kids love you a whole lot more.

Dad being on the road so much made him like a legend in our house. Like some kind of mythical hero. And because Mom was the one wrapped up with the actual parenting, Dad was able to be the *fun parent* whenever he *was* home. Which meant, of course, that us kids were crazy for him.

Plus, when he came back, he always brought us little gas station gifts and treats and stories from his time on the road. One time, he even brought us a puppy. The puppy was a little thing named Chico—black with curly fur and tufts of white on his paws.

Dad said that it was my dog. I was ecstatic.

Looking back on it, though, I only ended up playing with Chico a few times before he vanished. I'm not sure what happened to him. Maybe he was one of those mill puppies that ended up dying because of the terrible conditions of his birth. Maybe he ran away. Maybe Mom didn't want him and made Dad get rid of him.

I don't think I was that sad about losing Chico. At least, never as sad as I was to lose Dad.

Whenever Dad came home, I felt like I was seeing my best friend again after not hanging out in months. And when the time inevitably came for him to go back on the road, I was crushed.

Even though we were always more excited to see Dad walking through the side door of the house, I have to respect Mom and all the work that she did raising us. It could not have been easy to be a mother raising three kids alone. Even though she had a husband to help her financially with the bills, she did not have a father to help her emotionally with the children.

We all respected and behaved for Mom, so it isn't like we made her job especially difficult. And it's not like she was unable to manage us. But I still think that life could have been better for all of us if Dad was constantly in the picture to offer his support and guidance.

Mom loved Dad like we all did, though. She didn't hold his flightiness against him—which I guess is just another testament to the kind of woman that she was.

Even though I'm sure Mom and Dad fought like all adults do, I don't have any memories of them doing it in front of me or my siblings. To be fair, though, I don't have many memories of them in the same room.

When they were, they were usually in good spirits.

I think we all really felt my father's absence during the holidays, though. Dad tried his best to be around for the big ones—Christmas and birthdays—but even he was not perfect with this, and we ended up spending many Christmas days with just Mom, listening to The Jackson 5 little voices singing, *Have Yourself a Merry Little Christmas,* and feeling all too aware of the lyrics.

As a kid, I did not resent Dad for being absent. I didn't know that resenting your parents was something that you could do. I hated that he was never around. I hated that his lack of presence often led to things going on in the house that went unnoticed by the other adults around me. I always felt like if Dad had been home more often, then I wouldn't have had to endure some of the things that I suffered through because he would have been around to save me.

Still, though. For the longest time, I was not angry at *him* so much as I was angry at the circumstances that surrounded his lack of proximity to me.

But as I got older, my feelings around the situation became more and more complex. The feelings of abandonment I endured from the lack of a father figure in my life took root and erected a wall of disconnect between my dad and me. I grew to be more disconnected from him— even to the point where I stopped caring if I got to talk to him or not. He'd call sometimes from the road when he had a chance. When I was a little kid, I'd wrestle my siblings for a chance to talk to him first. But growing older, I found my desire to talk to him lessening—until sometimes, I didn't ask for the phone at all.

I started to feel like maybe Dad didn't love us all as much as I'd thought when I was younger—because if he *did* love us that much, wouldn't he be home more often?

I suppose that I only harbored this fear because I loved *him* so much that the thought of him not caring about me or my siblings pierced me like a knife to the heart.

Even as I was starting to distance myself from him, I still loved the man and looked up to him. I spoke in his defense more often than I care to admit. Nobody could say something bad about my dad with me around. I'd get upset and quickly correct whatever they'd said with the truth. Or, at least, the version of it that I wanted to believe.

Maybe because my dad was gone so often, I often found myself seeking approval from my uncle Quame. My uncle wasn't technically related to me by blood. He was my mother's sister's husband. But he was close with our family, and he was particularly good friends with my dad.

When he, my aunt, and my cousins would come over, I'd pester Uncle Quame with questions about Dad. *Have you talked to my dad recently? What did he say? Is he coming home soon? Does he know that we're waiting for him?*

My uncle would just laugh, wrap an arm around me, and remind me in that warm voice of his, "Your dad loves his kids so much, Feisal. Don't forget that."

I tried not to.

Times like this, when Dad and I just sat on the couch together watching movies, served as helpful reminders.

Some of my friends had Dads who didn't like to spend time with their families at all. Those dads would either spend all their time and money up at whatever bar was most convenient to stumble home from or they would lock themselves in their basements and play video games alone.

At least Dad spent the time that he did have at home with his kids. At least we got some of him instead of none of him at all.

As I tried to keep up with the movie's plot (movies like this were hard for kids to follow. Why was that guy named Dollar Bill and what in the world kind of animal is a loan shark?), I kept casting sideways glances at Dad. I was trying to meter his expression to know whether I should laugh, be quiet, or frown at whatever was happening on screen.

As the movie came to a slower part, I found myself asking, "Dad?"

A question had been on my mind throughout most of the film. It had been bugging me, chewing away at my throat like a termite chews wood.

Dad didn't glance away from the television. "What?"

"Why can't we watch movies like this all the time?" I asked. I tried to meter my tone. I didn't want to upset Dad with my question. I was just curious.

Dad's eyes flickered over to me for a brief moment. Maybe to see if I was being impudent. "It's not that simple, son," he said, after apparently deciding that my question was sincere enough to be answered. "When you're the man of the house, your first responsibility is your family's wellbeing. You've got to make sure they're fed, that they're clothed, and that there's a roof over their heads."

I nodded. Even though I did not understand the true gravity of what my father was saying (what child understands what *wellbeing* is anyway?), I knew that this was a very important matter to him.

"Going to work keeps you, your mama, and your siblings from going hungry. As much as I'd love to spend all the time in the world with you guys, keeping you all from starving is my first priority. And anyway, there's some dignity in a job you got to sacrifice a little bit for."

"Like a soldier?"

"Yeah," Dad seemed to like how that sounded. "Exactly."

"Okay."

He turned his attention back to Dollar Bill on the screen. "You're not going to understand it now, but you'll be thankful for me when you're older."

As I looked up at the screen, I felt a little twist in my stomach.

Would I be thankful for my father when I was older?

Most of me believed that this was true. But the smallest, most traitorous part of my brain—the part that I did not want to even acknowledge at the time—warned me: *you might not.*

I pushed that evil little voice down. I didn't want to think about not being the perfect, grateful son. I just wanted to watch a movie with my dad. And I wanted to believe that more good times like this would be on the horizon.

God, did I want to believe that.

Chapter 4

FORT FUN

As much as I adored my dad growing up, my mom was an equally bright force in my life. Maybe even a little brighter.

Yvette, my mom, was a firecracker woman who had been born and raised in Virginia. She was raised by two hardworking but private people—and like me, most of her childhood was built and nurtured by her mother. Mom always described Grandma as tough and maybe even a bit intimidating, but a fierce lover and advocate for her babies.

Mom's family was big. She had six siblings in total—though she was only especially close to two of them: her sister, Nina, and her brother, Carl.

Though Mom never finished high school, she never shied away from hard work. Over the course of her life, she'd worked dutifully as a bank supervisor. And, of course, as the mother of three kids.

She'd met Dad during one hot summer when he'd been stationed in Virginia as a part of his military service. Despite being young, they fell in love quickly and spared no time in getting married and having kids. Sometimes I wonder if

Mom ever had flashes of doubt about Dad. If she ever looked at him only to catch some dark premonition of the future glittering in his eyes. Had she seen the man who he was behind the smiles and good humor, I wonder if she still would have tried for a life with him.

This is a question that I do not really want the answer to.

One thing about my mom's family that I didn't know about until older in life was the long river of illness that seemed to run through it.

Mom had lost one of her younger sisters the year that she and Dad got married. She'd perished due to a heart disease—though I don't know which one. Shortly after, she'd be struck by another tragic loss. Two years after I was born, her father passed away from some kind of incurable illness.

Nobody ever knew what the illness actually was. Grandpa was secretive and did not take a shine to the thought of anybody but himself and his general practitioner knowing his health business. And I'm sure that even the practitioner was on thin ice.

Unlike Dad, Mom was around us all the time. And for raising three kids virtually alone, she did a damn fine job. Mom eventually stopped working at the bank. Even though she could not provide for the family financially anymore, she had a job—and hers was a job that never paused, rested, or allowed a day off.

She cooked. She cleaned. She made sure that our shirts were not on inside-out.

And she was fun, too.

Me and my siblings all played baseball as kids. Rhondelle played softball for a team called the Bumblebees while Wayne and I played t-ball for a team called the Cardinals. Every Wednesday night, Mom would drive us to our practices and watch us do pop-fly drills from the stands.

On the weekends when we had games, Mom could always be seen in the bleachers cheering us kids on. After games, Mom would take us to the concession stand to order nachos and slushies as a prize for winning or as a consolation prize for losing.

Wayne and I only lost one game, to the Blue Jays. It was one of our last of the season. I think that we were just bummed about the season ending and performed poorly because of a lack of morale.

At the end of the season, we got bobblehead trophies.

On top of supporting our athletics, Mom also made sure that our lack of money to go on trips didn't stop us from having a good time. I remember her taking us to this park called Fort Fun.

Lord, did I love Fort Fun. It was this wooden playground set about a block away from the baseball fields. About five black tires were nailed to the side of the playground set. The woodchips that padded the ground around the playset always got stuck to our socks and our clothes. In the hot of the summer, carpenter bees would swarm the playground.

Mom, Wayne, Rhondelle, and I used to run around Fort Fun before and after our practices, playing hide 'n seek and tag. I remember the weather always being nice. I remember us always laughing and smiling.

Sometimes, I wonder if the memory of Fort Fun strikes as clear a chord in the memories of my siblings as it does in me.

For the longest time, the park faded into the back of my memory. Then, one day as I was taking a trip back to Virginia, the name popped into my head as clear as day. I wanted to drive back to the baseball fields to see if the old park was still standing—and if it looked the same now as it did in my memory—but I was on a crunch for time and could not fit the extra stop into my itinerary.

To this day, I regret not going.

Fort Fun was one of the best memories of my childhood. I'd do just about anything to see it again. Maybe one day I'll get Wayne and Rhondelle and some flowers for Mom, and we can all take a trip down.

Hopefully by then, the park is still around. If it's not, I'm not quite sure what I'll do with myself.

In all my memories of her, Mom wore jewelry. She loved her necklaces, bracelets, and rings. She'd wear so many shiny bracelets at a time that I swore a well-aimed flashlight would turn her wrist into a disco ball. She never made them look tacky, though. Everything looked good on Mom.

She also had piercings. Mom had her ears, tongue, nose, eyebrow, and belly button pierced. She never wore all her piercings at once. Some days, she'd dial it back to a pair of chunky earrings and a stud in her nose. Other days, she sported a ring in her eyebrows and a spiky plastic ball in her tongue.

Mom matched her piercings with her outfits. And she matched her outfits to the occasion. She never donned something too casual or too fancy. Like Goldilocks and the Three Bears, Mom had a sixth sense for *just right.*

As a kid, I especially loved Mom's earrings. Mom wore hoops that were almost as big and heavy as her bracelets. I used to tug on them, wondering idly if they hurt to wear.

One time, she stopped me. "Feisal, you've got to stop that. You're going to pull them out." Her voice was firm but kind.

"Sorry." I quickly retracted my hand but kept my eyes on the sparkly hoop.

Mom studied my face for a bit. Then, a *look* passed over her face. "You like my earrings?"

I nodded. And I wasn't just bluffing because she was my mom. I genuinely did like her earrings. I thought they made her look elegant.

Mom's lip curved up. "I can pierce one of your ears if you want. You can match with me."

"Really?" The thought excited me. A piercing of my own? Yes, please.

I had no misbelief that certain things were just for boys or just for girls. Well, maybe I believed that about things like dresses or dolls. But not earrings. After all, there were plenty of boys that wore earrings—from Snoop to Tupac. A couple of boys at my school had earrings, too. There were some murmurings among them about wearing the earring on the "correct" side, but that was all.

So, with my happy enthusiasm, Mom prepared a makeshift piercing salon in our bathroom with a sewing needle, one of her more masculine-looking studs, and an ice cube. The process was painful, but thanks to my mom's deft hands, it didn't take very long to finish. And soon, I was examining my ear in the mirror, my eyes drawn to the stark contrast of the sparkling diamond stud in my dark skin and the little trickle of blood dripping down from it.

"We've got to keep it clean," Mom said. "Otherwise, it'll get infected. So, don't go playing out in the dirt for a few days. You understand me?"

I nodded diligently. I didn't want anything jeopardizing my new piercing. I thanked Mom and hugged her. Then, I went outside to go show my friends.

Dad was not happy about the pierced ear. I don't know what about it ticked him off. Maybe it was the fact that Mom had done it without his permission. Maybe he just didn't think that pierced ears were appropriate for his boys to have.

It might have been the fact that I had both pierced ears *and* braids.

Whatever it was, Dad quickly decided to get back at Mom by chopping my braids off himself. As I watched my long hair sit in an unceremonious clump on the kitchen floor after Dad had gone at it with a pair of scissors and clippers, I started to understand that Dad was not somebody to play around with. He had little restraint, and a firm belief that whatever he did was just. That combination made it impossible to fight his fire with anything but calm and complete deference.

Little did I know at the time that this act of vengeance from my father was a mere predecessor for what was soon to come.

Chapter 5

THE BALLETIC COLLAPSE

"You paying attention, Feisal?" Mom's voice was light and lilted as she sat across from me on my Aunt Nina's guest bed.

We were staying over at my aunt's house for a long weekend. Mom had just started the long process of braiding my sister's dark hair. Ever the curious kid, I come up to watch. Mom never discouraged my interest in things like this. Never shooed me away or told me that it wasn't right for a male to care about how to braid hair properly.

Oldies played over Nina's stereo system in the living room, somewhat muffled. It was a warm day.

I was perfectly content watching Mom show me the intricacies of braiding. My eyes studied her deft hands as she demonstrated the separation of a patch of hair into three strands, and then the weaving of those strands into the finished braid.

After she'd done a good chunk of my sister's head, she scooted over, instructing me to try my hand at the process. Mom placed her fingers over mine as we slowly finished my sister's hair. Rhondelle chattered excitably and squirmed as the braiding took twice as long as normal. I don't remember a thing she said.

All I remember is the confident way my mother moved. Her unshakable hands. Her proud guidance.

It was the last time I ever saw Mom look quite so sure of herself. And it was one of the last things that we did together before everything started to go wrong.

When we returned to our house from my aunt's, Mom remarked that she was tired. She wanted to lay down, she said. I thought that it was unusual because Mom was not usually tired so early in the afternoon.

Regardless, when she asked me to help her carry her bag back to her room, I agreed. Quietly, I followed Mom down the long hallway leading up to her bedroom. As soon as we stepped in, Mom collapsed on the bed.

As in, *literally* collapsed.

It was as if Mom had somehow foreseen her own weakness and thought to find a way to pad her inevitable fall.

Either way, even at eight, I was keen enough to realize that something was terribly wrong. I dropped Mom's bag on the floor and rushed over to her.

"Mom?" I shook her arm. "Are you okay? What happened?"

Mom didn't respond to my shaking. Even though she had been conscious and moving no more than five seconds ago, she was now completely out. I shook her with more force, my heartbeat growing more and more frantic with every second of silence that passed.

Realizing that this was a problem far beyond my capabilities to solve, I raced out of Mom's room and screamed for Aunt Nina, who was still in the driveway. My little voice tore out of my throat, and Nina jumped into action, quickly rushing into the house to assess the situation.

My aunt must have dialed 911. I don't really recall her picking up the house phone or making the call, though. All I remember is a swarm of paramedics surrounding Mom, lifting her up onto a stretcher.

Helpless, I just stood there.

I had never seen someone collapse like that in my entire life. Not even on TV. Looking back, I am sure that my fear was more instinctual than anything else. Even though I had no knowledge of what was happening, the all-consuming pit in my gut told me everything that I needed to know.

With a stiff sense of professionalism, the paramedics quickly hauled Mom away. Not one of them spoke to me. I don't think that it would've mattered if they had—I'm not sure I would have registered the sounds coming from their mouths as intelligent words.

While Mom went to the hospital, my siblings and I stayed home. A blur of family members—grandmothers, aunts, cousins, etc.—shuffled in and out of the house, ensuring that my siblings and I were not left unattended. They tried to care for us, but I was still too stunned by the shock. Wayne and Rhondelle were too young to understand anything that was happening.

Eventually, one of my cousins offered to take us to the hospital so that we could visit Mom.

"Doesn't that sound like a good idea?" the cousin asked us.

No! I wanted to scream. *No! I don't want to go to the hospital. I just want Mom to come home.*

I have always hated hospitals. As a child, I hated them especially so.

I could not yet fully conceptualize the concept of *death* at that age. But somewhere in my primal animal brain, the connection between hospitals and death was as poignant and visceral as any.

Everything about hospitals reeked of death to me. From the nondescript, Limbo-like hallways, to the unnaturally sharp smell of the alcohol wipes. The fact that there was a prayer room in the hospital didn't help things. Why, if hospitals did not mean death, did they come pre-built with a hotline directly connected to the Big Man himself?

Except I didn't have the words back then to express exactly *why* I did not want to see my mom in the hospital. And my cousin was looking at me expectantly as if I should have been jumping on the opportunity to go as a wild beast jumps on his next meal. So, cautiously, I nodded my affirmative.

Unsurprisingly, I hated every second of the visit.

Seeing my mom in her hospital bed broke my heart. The woman had collapsed only days earlier, and yet, when my siblings and I walked in, she somehow found the strength to put a smile on her face.

Mom seemingly did not care that she was in pain. She did not care that her health had taken a severe and dramatic turn for the worse. All she cared about was making sure that her kids did not feel afraid or worried for her.

I wish that her smile could've relieved me of my worry the way that I'm sure she wanted it to.

The truth was that I had always been worried about Mom. I do not ever recall being told about my mother's illness, but somehow, I'd had the creeping sense anyway that something bad was going to happen to her. There were some occasions before her collapse where I'd just stare at her, my brows drawn and my lips pursed, a quietly buzzing mess of anxiety.

I couldn't help but worry. When you're a kid, your parents are your world. I loved Dad, but Mom was my rock. If something happened to her, I didn't know what I'd do.

I was always a little protective of Mom regardless.

Mom used to let Rhondelle and I take turns going to work with her. I'd always feel so angry and jealous on the days when Rhondelle went instead of me. Mom knew that I wanted to go with her, but she was dedicated to being a fair matriarch.

There were times when a classmate or a cousin's birthday would pop up, and Mom would take my siblings and me with her to the store so that we could pick out a gift for them. As I perused the aisles of Hot Wheels and Tonka Trucks, I often reckoned with a subtle prickling sensation of jealousy at the fact that Mom was sharing her love and warmth with someone other than Rhondelle, Wayne, or me. I'd get over the agony quickly, of course. But the point was that the idea of sharing Mom was aggravating.

Thus, the idea of *losing* her was unfathomable.

As I listened to Mom croon and coo at us kids, assuring us that everything was okay and that she'd be home soon, I forced myself to believe her. Even though I could see a little flicker of doubt in her eyes. Even though I could feel it in the pit of my soul that she was lying.

As our cousin took us to the elevator, I felt my stomach clench.

Leaving Mom was terrible. Not to mention the fact that I was downright terrified of elevators. I balled my fists as my cousin clicked the button for us to go back down to the first floor. The elevator jerked to life. My heart rate quickened.

I was never quite afraid of getting stuck in elevators. People got stuck in elevators all the time and lived to tell the tale. In fact, that was the purpose of the little button with the fireman's hat at the bottom of the control panel. If you got stuck, you could call someone strong and brave to come and save you.

No, the thing that I was afraid of was falling.

I always had this vision of getting in an elevator and the steel cable snapping. The elevator would plummet to the ground, and I'd have to jump out to save myself like the hero in some kind of action movie.

Even when I was a kid, I knew that if the elevator fell with you in it, there was nothing that you could do to stop it. No fireman in the world could come and save you fast enough. The only defense left, then, would be to close your eyes and pray to God and hope against hope that he listened.

Chapter 6

Sickle Hell

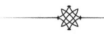

*M*om finally returned from the hospital on a chilly fall night. It was several weeks after we'd come to visit her.

Foolishly, I hoped that this meant everything would go back to normal. Wayne, Rhondelle, and I had been sick plenty of times. After the initial fever or flu went away, we'd be fine—back to our normal selves.

I had the instinct to know that Mom's collapse hadn't been a simple cold. Yet, I also had the naivete to believe that it could be something equally as harmless.

Those hopes were dashed the moment I saw Mom come in through the front door. She was being pushed into the house in a wheelchair by some stranger. Mom wore a pair of navy-blue sweatpants. Her hair was brushed back and out of the way. She had no makeup on. And most damning of all: she had no jewelry on, either.

She was swollen. Extremely swollen. She could barely open her eyes wide enough to see me.

Whatever was ailing her had also taken a toll on her body. Before her sickness, Mom had been a petite woman—

never exceeding 120 pounds. The newly disabled woman before me looked to be nearly two times that weight.

It shattered me to see her like that. It wasn't the fact that she'd gained weight that bothered me. It was the fact that she'd gained weight as a result of something that had to do with an illness that was completely out of her power and that had apparently spiraled out of control overnight.

At that moment, as I watched Mom settle back into our house with the help of the medical aide, I realized that my dreams of things going back to the way they used to be were officially gone. Things would never go back to the way they used to be. Mom would never be the healthy, vibrant, jubilant woman that she'd been before.

This was life now. There was no turning back. No rewinding.

All I could do was learn to keep moving forward.

Mom had something called *edema*. As a kid, I didn't know what edema was, nor did I know what caused it. Now that I am older, I understand it more. Edema is what happens when fluid gets trapped in the body, causing swelling. It can happen anywhere, but it's most likely to target parts of the body below the waist.

Edema is a very broad term, referring to any kind of unnatural fluid-related swelling in the body. So, it can be caused by any number of things. Pregnancy, heart disease, genetics—all of it can lead down the same painful road.

Mom's edema was specifically caused by complications of sickle cell anemia.

When edema gets to the vital organs—specifically the lungs—it can be life-threatening.

The disease is a painful, ugly affair. My mother, in all her perfect kindness, did not deserve it. And yet, she had gotten it anyway thanks to a bad roll of some cosmic dice.

Time did eventually start moving forward again. With my mom back in the house, the hazy fog in my mind began to cede. Things would never be the *same,* but normal *could* be redefined. I tried not to let my new reality bother me. Even though it was a marked devolvement from the life that I had once known, I knew that it was no use being miserable over it. Plus, however bad *I* was feeling, I was sure that Mom felt worse.

Mom's edema began to show itself in little, minute ways. Mom always had to ask my siblings and me for things now. Everything from big chores, helping her with cleaning or dusting or vacuuming; to little chores, grabbing the remote or getting her a glass of water. I could always see in her eyes that it pained her to ask these tasks of us. I could almost hear her thinking, *I am their mother! I should be the one taking care of them.*

Wayne was too young at the time to understand the change. He didn't get why Mom now made her way around the house in a wheelchair or why she couldn't push herself up on her legs to grab something five feet away from her.

Rhondelle tried her best to cope. I know that it must have hurt her to see Mom like that. Like me, she looked up to Mom greatly and it killed her a little to see Mom reduced to a shell of her former self.

Rhondelle and I tried to comfort each other through it, but as we were both only kids, our attempts at soothing were mostly well-intentioned but poorly executed. The thing is, we didn't need each other. We needed an adult. And because Mom was learning to cope herself and couldn't be the strong rock of emotional stability that we craved, we needed *Dad.* But Dad wasn't home. He never was.

After Mom came back from the hospital, our family started coming by a lot more often. They did their best to take care of us and support Mom, but it was clear that almost everyone was just as clueless as Rhondelle, Wayne, and me. Our phone was always ringing after that hospital visit. Aunties checked in and offered food. Grandparents asked for updates on Mom's condition and warned us not to trust doctors.

Mom hated the company. She didn't want people to see her in her sickened state.

Most people who knew my mom were used to seeing her as a jubilant and boundless force. Full of energy, quick to smile, and always gracious with her wit. She used to jump in her car on a moment's notice and tear down the street, the sound of tires squealing and motors purring following her wherever she went.

Mom's favorite car was a royal blue Cadillac. God, she loved that damn car. She had it forever—until a drunk motorcyclist rammed into the left side.

I remember it like it was yesterday: Mom and I were coming home from my aunt's house. Rhondelle, Wayne, and I were sitting in the back seat, and Mom was in the front. She was playing some top-40s pop hit, the kind that you somehow know all the words to even if you've never heard the song outside of the radio.

It was getting dark out, but we were all in good spirits. It had been a good day.

At some point, Mom took a U-turn. She was straightening out of her turn when a loud, sudden jolt rocked the car. Whatever had impacted the car had hit it on *my* side. I flinched, covering myself instinctively with my hands.

Mom braked immediately and parked the car. She fumbled for her seatbelt and hopped out. Gathering my senses, I peered out the side window to look at the idiot who had just hit us. He was an older guy. Bald, with a potbelly and a short-sleeved shirt. He swayed slightly, side to side, as Mom helped him up.

I could hear them talking dimly through the car window.

"...you okay?"

"Yeah, I'm okay... sorry. I've had a rough night... been at the bar for most of it..."

My eyes widened. Had this fool been *drinking?* No wonder he crashed right into us! I glared at him through the window, wanting to punch him right in his stupid, hairless face.

Mom didn't call the cops on the man. I don't know why she didn't.

When she got back into the car, the first words out of her mouth were, "Are you kids okay?"

We all nodded. Of course, we were. The hit had scared us more than anything else. Physically, all of our hearts were still beating, our lungs were still pumping, and our blood was still flowing. We were fine.

Mom apologized to us—for what, I don't know—and cautiously drove us the rest of the way home. As we cruised down the dark streets, I peered out the windows, my sense of responsibility driving me to keep a keen watch of our surroundings, just in case any other idiots wanted to show themselves.

When we got back to the house, I surveyed the damage that had been done to the car. The motorcycle guy had been going fast enough to leave an ugly scratch and dent—but thankfully had not totaled the vehicle.

It would continue to drive if we let it.

Except Mom was not interested in driving around in a busted car. Shortly after the accident, she took it in and traded it for a new one.

I had the feeling that she wanted to do that to *herself* now. Take herself back into the hospital and trade herself in for a shiny, clean mother for us kids.

But I wouldn't have let her. Just as she loved her shiny Cadillac, I loved her. And I wasn't going to let some stupid drunk idiot called *Sickle Cell* take her away from us.

As time went on, we did learn to cope with Mom's new state of existence. Uncle Carl, my mom's brother, moved in early on to help around the house. His most burdensome duty was that of carrying Mom up and down the stairs whenever she needed it.

For some reason, there was no bathroom downstairs in our house.

Once you walked in, you were met with the living room. To the right, you'd find some stairs leading up to the second floor. To the left, you'd see the kitchen and the laundry room.

The second floor housed the bedrooms. My parents had the largest bedroom, Wayne and I shared a medium-sized room (we used to have our own spaces, but when Uncle Carl moved in to help with Mom, I had to move in with Wayne), and Rhondelle had the littlest room of all. Once you got past the bedrooms, *then* you'd find the bathroom.

Sharing one bathroom amongst five people almost made me thankful during the times when Dad wasn't home.

Uncle Carl stayed in the house for a while to take care of Mom. Multiple times throughout the day, I'd see him carrying her up and down the stairs because her edema meant that it hurt too much for her to do it herself.

Carl would help Mom to the bathroom, and then I'd be called to help clean her.

The first time Mom had asked me for help with cleaning her, I felt a strange sense of awkwardness. I had never, ever needed to clean another person. Not even my siblings. And now, I needed to clean my mother?

Shit, I was still learning how to clean *myself.*

I was a little hesitant at first—but eventually, I realized that the chore wasn't going away. That all I could do was buckle down and help Mom in whatever way I could. After a couple of times, cleaning Mom became as routine and as normal as taking out the trash. It was never something that I wanted to do, but never something I complained about, either.

Deep down, I think I could sense that Mom was embarrassed about having to have her son clean her. If I reacted funny, she'd only feel worse.

I also had to help Mom with bed baths. She couldn't stand up in the bathtub to take her own showers, and so baths had to be done with a damp washcloth in her bed.

My heart broke a little every time I had to give her a bed bath. Just a few weeks ago, Mom had been able to do this work herself. She had been a fully autonomous woman. And now, she needed to depend on someone else. Her son, at that.

There were a few shimmers of joy throughout the whole ordeal.

One of them was my brother, Wayne. At the time, Wayne was too young to know anything that was happening. He couldn't understand what Mom was going through. So, when he looked at her, it was not with the usual air of pity or sorrow.

There was this one time that I was helping Mom with her medications. Wayne watched next to me as I handed Mom her pills and a glass of water. Mom threw her head back to make it easier to swallow the pills.

Something about the dramaticism of her head-throw put Wayne in stitches. He laughed exuberantly. He laughed so damn hard, that Mom and I laughed too, despite ourselves.

After that, Mom began purposely throwing her head back even when there were no pills to swallow. And every time, it made Wayne crack up. And every time, we would crack up right with him.

Before my mom's health started declining, she often took us to Aunt Nina's house to play with our favorite cousins.

Mom and Nina were not only sisters but also best friends. They could sit for hours in the kitchen talking over coffee or giggling about some long-gone story about their high school years.

If we weren't at Nina's house over the weekend, Nina was at ours.

One of our favorite games to play was school. All of us kids would pick our subject, and we'd all take turns being in charge of class. I always chose to be the gym teacher. I'd make us do exercises like jumping jacks and push-ups. Sometimes, Mom and Nina would even join as "transfer students."

I made them do jumping jacks and push-ups, too.

During this time, nobody would've been able to tell that Mom was secretly suffering health issues. She could keep up with all of us. She could walk perfectly fine. She managed the hustle and bustle of life, taking us kids to our sports games and playing with us at Fort Fun, without missing a single beat.

She always kept a good mood. Even when I'm sure the cells sickling beneath the surface made it difficult.

At night, she'd corral all of us kids into the living room to watch scary movies with her. I always loved these movie nights. Sometimes, Mom would start to nod off in the middle of the film, and I'd have to do whatever it took to keep her awake.

I had my strategies for this. Sometimes I would ask her to scratch my back. Other times, I would pretend that a fleck of dust had gotten in my eye, and I needed her help to get rid of it. Mom would blow on my eye, and I would rub it, and then I would complain that rubbing it had made it worse. Mom, of course, knew what I was up to. But she entertained me nonetheless, which is what really mattered.

Mom's favorite trick was to pretend that she needed to leave the room for something so that she could scare us. One time, she claimed that she needed to get some "water." She went downstairs to get herself a glass.

We were watching *Halloween* with Michael Myers, so my siblings and I were already a little antsy. After a few minutes, Wayne tugged on my pajama shirt sleeve and said, "Mom's not back yet. Should we go look for her?"

Rhondelle and I agreed that we should look for Mom. Carefully, we tiptoed down the stairs. Maybe it was my nervous energy from watching *Halloween*, but I felt like the house was twice as dark as it usually was.

As soon as we got down the stairs and turned to enter the kitchen, Mom jumped out from behind a shelf wearing a clown mask. *"AHHH!"* she screamed.

I could've died right then and there.

In fact, I think a little piece of my soul left my body on that night—never to return again.

Now as an adult looking back, I almost kind of miss that clown mask. It was a little misshapen and smelled like rotting latex. The slightly messed-up nose reminded me of the clown from Stephen King's *IT*.

Mom watched scary movies with us almost every night. At this point, I've probably seen just about every slasher, every psychological thriller, and every demonic possession film ever shot and produced on DVD.

After we finished our movie, Mom would take us to bed. Every night, she would tuck us in and say, "I love you. Goodnight."

She said it to each of us individually. Down the hall, I would always be able to hear Rhondelle and Wayne's small voices chirp back, "Love you too, Mommy."

But then she'd come to my room and say the same thing to me, but I wouldn't be able to say it back. Mom would just give me a gentle look, knowing that even if I didn't say it out loud, I meant it inside.

I don't know why it was so hard for me to tell my mother that I loved her.

The issue wasn't exclusive to bedtime. I had a hard time saying "I love you" to Mom regardless of the circumstances. Every time Mom said she loved me, I would just respond with silence. My face would burn, because I'd feel like an idiot. What kind of son couldn't tell his own mother that he loved her?

Mom never shamed me for not saying it, but I always wondered if it hurt her.

It wasn't like I didn't know *how* to say it. I understood the words, "I love you," and I knew what they meant. I also loved Mom more than anyone and anything in the world. But for whatever reason, whenever Mom told me that she loved me, I'd find those three little words lodged in my throat, unable to escape.

So, instead of telling Mom that I loved her, I smiled instead.

And I tried to channel all the love I'd ever had for Mom into those smiles. I smiled so fondly and so sincerely that I could feel the affection *radiating* out of my mouth.

But still, it wasn't the same as saying the words aloud. And it never felt like enough.

This anxiety around the words "I love you" didn't change after Mom's sickness took hold. Honestly, it might've gotten worse.

As Mom became more and more disabled, I found myself more and more responsible for the things around the house that needed done. I didn't loathe the responsibility, but sometimes I found it frustrating.

Especially because I was the oldest, so it felt like the burden laid heaviest upon my shoulders.

There was this one time that I wanted desperately to hang out with my friends. It was a sunny Saturday—warm, but not sweltering—and I'd already finished all of my homework ahead of time. The world was mine. Or, at least, it *should* have been.

But before I could run out to join my friends for a game of basketball, Mom stopped me.

"Feisal," she said, her voice gentle, "I need some help, honey. Can you stay in for a little?"

My heart sank in my chest.

No! I wanted to yell. *No! I just want to play. I want to be a kid for once. Can't I do that?*

But I stayed quiet.

"What do you need, Mom?" I asked her, trying like hell to keep any trace of resentment out of my tone.

Mom looked down at her swollen legs. She told me that she needed my help to massage them. She was in pain and her meds weren't helping. The only thing that could bring her any relief, she'd said, was for me to massage them for her.

This was not the first time that Mom had asked me to massage her legs. I'd done it several times before. It always upset me to do because Mom's edema was so bad that my hands left full impressions in her swollen, fluid-filled legs. But I'd been worn down over the past several weeks of helping Mom, and the thought of having my playtime derailed by her illness left me bitter and upset.

"Mom, I want to go outside and play," I said, donning a bit of an attitude. "Can't I just do it later?"

A bit of pain flashed through Mom's eyes. It was clear that she felt just terrible. Mom was not a selfish woman. She knew what she was doing. She knew that asking me to help her meant tearing me away from my fleeting weekend hours. But she also knew that she was hurting—and she wouldn't have asked a request of me if she didn't absolutely need it.

If Dad were home, he could have taken care of her.

But he wasn't. And so, the responsibility fell on me. It wasn't fair, but it was the reality of the situation.

Mom sighed. "Honey, I will *pay* you to massage my legs for me. Please."

At that moment, I felt like the worst son ever. My own Mom had to bribe me to take care of her. I could feel my heart shattering, breaking into a million tiny pieces. Suddenly, I couldn't be by her side fast enough.

I ended up staying with Mom. I sat at her side and massaged her legs as we watched TV together.

By the time I'd finished massaging her, I'd forgotten all about the money. When I was a child, money was everything to me. There was nothing I wanted more than those precious green dollar bills. So, I should have remembered that Mom had promised to pay me.

But I didn't.

I think that I was mature for my age. And that I would have rather spent the time with my mom anyway. Whether or not I was going to get paid for it, and whether or not I was going to miss out on a game of hockey with my friends.

From that day on, I never again gave my mom attitude whenever she asked me to do anything for her. I didn't roll my eyes or mouth off. I didn't even feel particularly bitter on the inside.

Something inside of me knew, even then, that soon I would no longer need to help Mom anymore. As her sickness advanced, it became clear that her time was running out. Going to school began to strike me with a buzzing anxiety: *What if I come home and Mom isn't waiting for us? What if she passes away while I'm in gym class? What if I don't even get a chance to say goodbye?*

I wanted to cherish every second that I had with her. Shit, Mom could have asked me to push a boulder up a hill, and I would've gladly done it—so long as she'd be there to watch me.

That night, Wayne, Rhondelle, and I went to Mom's room to wish her goodnight. Because she could no longer move on her own, we had to come to her if we wanted to hear her tell us, "I love you. Goodnight."

Mom kissed Wayne and Rhondelle on the forehead. She wished them goodnight. She told them that she loved them. As always, they repeated the tender phrase back to her before scurrying off to their rooms.

I was last. Mom hugged me.

"Thank you again for staying with me, Feisal," she said. "Goodnight. I love you."

I pulled back, staring at Mom with a huge smile on my face. She smiled right back at me, and there was an undeniable hum in the air.

This was it. The night that I'd finally tell Mom that I loved her right back. I could feel the words bubbling in my chest. I felt like a tea kettle on low heat, finally about to cry out the words that I had been holding on to for so long.

But just when I was about to say it, a floorboard in the house creaked. I turned to the hallway. I couldn't see who had disturbed the moment between Mom and me—but when I turned back to her, I knew that something had shifted. The energy from before was gone.

I'd lost my chance.

I uttered a quick, "Goodnight," to Mom. Then, without saying anything more, I ran off to the room I shared with Wayne.

That night, I lay in bed, staring up at the ceiling and cursing that stupid creaking floorboard for ruining my chance to tell Mom that I loved her. Even then, I knew in my chest. The truth was as sure as death and taxes: I'd never get a chance like that again.

Nowadays, I'd give anything to be able to tell Mom how much I love her. If I could see her again, I'd say the words over and over again until my throat went dry. *I love you, I love you, I love you.*

Or maybe I wouldn't. Maybe I'd just look at her and smile, as I'd always done.

I love you.

And she'd smile back, a brilliant sparkle of clarity in her eyes.

I know you do.

Chapter 7

99 PROBLEMS AND YOUR DADDY AIN'T ONE

*M*om's sickle cell didn't just deteriorate her body. It also deteriorated her relationship with Dad. And it also deteriorated us kids a little bit, too.

Even Wayne, I could see, was starting to look a little older and more tired than some of the other kids in his grade. He was still always a ball of energy and laughter—but there was a difference to it now. He was being exposed to something that most people don't experience until they are old enough to do their own taxes. We all were.

Life felt lonely at our little house.

Family came and went. Uncle Carl checked in often and so did Aunt Nina. But even though people *helped,* nobody really understood. Nobody at school knew what it was like to have to take care of an ailing mother. Nobody knew how awful it felt to hear her crying through the thin walls of the house because she was in so much pain.

I had my siblings to relate to. But even then, I couldn't help but feel like they just didn't *get it.* They were younger than me. Less mature. Less weighed down with the responsibility of it all.

And at the same time, I didn't get them. All of us were experiencing Mom's decline very differently, and none of us were wise enough yet to provide any real comfort to one another.

Without Mom to fill the role of both mother and father for us kids, Dad's absence became even more pronounced. I went from seeing him every few weeks to every few months. He rarely called to check in with us like before. And when he did, he always seemed distracted. Like there was something else more pressing and interesting to do, and calling his kids was just an obstacle in the way of that thing.

At first, this took a toll on me. I felt like I was losing my mom and my dad at the same time. But eventually, I grew numb to it.

I stopped caring about Dad. I stopped wondering where he was. I stopped looking forward to his brief returns home. I blamed him for not finding work closer to home so that he could care for Mom. I resented the fact that I had to pick up his slack.

Didn't Uncle Quame say that Dad loved us? Was that all a lie?

It was starting to seem like one.

Now, in retrospect, I realize that my parents had gone their separate ways at that point. Dad had little emotional obligation to Mom.

Still, that didn't change the fact that he should've been around. If not for his wife, whom he'd sworn before God to love in sickness and in health—then for his kids, who needed him desperately.

All hell broke loose on one chilly winter night, prior to Mom's decline.

Rhondelle had just gotten back home from visiting Dad out of town. She'd had a long holiday from school, and Dad had made the unusually fatherly decision to take her out on the road with him for the weekend.

Had I been younger and less jaded with Dad, I might've been jealous of the quality time that she got to spend with him. But at the time, I was so fed up with him that I couldn't care less.

When Rhondelle finally walked back through our front door, she seemed relieved to be back. I was upstairs in my room getting ready for bed, but I could still hear her high-pitched little voice coming through the walls as she jogged up the stairs to greet Mom.

Mom's initial response was not quite as warm, however.

"Rhondelle," Mom's voice was almost stern. "What happened to your hair? This isn't how I did it before you left."

I could almost see Mom's face, twisted in a mix of horror and mild disgruntlement, as she took Rhondelle's hair in her fingers.

Rhondelle paused for a second. Then she said, "Oh, Daddy's friend did it. She changed my hair."

Rhondelle was obviously young at the time. She couldn't have understood the gravity of what she was saying. She probably didn't even fully realize that Daddy's *friend* was probably actually his *girlfriend.*

I heard Mom shift. "What friend? Your Dad has a friend?"

"Yeah. She's nice," Rhondelle said.

Oh, that did it. Mom gasped. *"She?!* So, it's a woman? Rhondelle, you better be telling me the truth right now."

As mature of a kid as I was, nosiness was not above me. I snuck up to my bedroom door, pressing my ear against it to hear the conversation better. I wasn't sure what was going on, but I was sure from the rising sound of my Mom's voice that Rhondelle was in trouble. Big trouble.

Except Mom didn't punish Rhondelle. She didn't even yell at her. She just sighed and said, "Okay. Thank you. Go to bed, honey. Good night." And of course, Mom couldn't forget her customary, "I love you."

Rhondelle cautiously returned an "I love you," before zipping off to her room.

My room was between Mom and Rhondelle's. Rhondelle saw me watching her as she retreated. I gave her an accusatory look, which she responded to with a wide-eyed shrug. As if to say, *don't look at me like that! I don't know what's going on either!*

Rhondelle had closed Mom's door on her way out, but I could still hear Mom's voice through the crack at the bottom as she called up Dad's phone. I could even sort of hear Dad's nonchalant voice as it came through the speaker when he picked up.

Mom had no time for pleasantries. She made it immediately clear that she did not have the patience for any foolishness.

"So, who's this woman touching my daughter's hair, Jamal?" She demanded.

Dad said something incomprehensible. Mom didn't let him finish.

"Nuh-uh. She said you had a friend. A *female* friend. Do you think I'm stupid?" A pause. "Who is she, Jamal? Are you with this girl when you're on the road? When you're supposed to be working?" Another pause. And then a sigh. "How long have you been seeing her?"

I couldn't really hear how Dad was responding, but I could tell that he was being evasive because Mom kept grilling him with the same few questions.

What is her name?

How long have you been seeing her?

Where is she from?

Is she driving around in your truck with you?

Is she there with you right now?

Eventually, Mom hung up. She slammed the phone down on her side table. I waited with my breath held at my door, wondering what was going to happen next. Would Dad call to apologize? Was Mom going to call an emergency family meeting to let us know that we would be packing our things and running away forever?

But after a few minutes, Mom shut off her nightstand lamp, and I realized that nothing was going to happen. Or, if it was, it at least wasn't going to happen on that night.

Nothing would happen the next night either. Or the night after that. But one day, as we sat in the kitchen, JAY-Z's song, *99 Problems* would come on the radio. Every time JAY-Z said, "I got 99 problems, but a bitch ain't one," Mom would replace the lyrics and say, "I got 99 problems and your daddy ain't one."

I smirked at that, shaking my head. Even after everything that had happened, Mom was still as classy as ever.

Chapter 8

SEIZE THE CONVULSIONS.
UNDER-DOSE

For a while, Mom's declining health became something like background noise. We certainly didn't like it, but we'd gotten used to it. Time rendered us almost a little numb to Mom's condition. We knew that she wasn't doing well. Even little Wayne knew that by then. But nothing in our power could change the way her body worked. All we could do was wake up, brush our teeth, go to school, come home, eat dinner, and go to sleep. Then, we'd wake up the next morning and do it all over again.

It's a little funny, man's ability to adapt to anything. On one hand, I was grateful that slipping into a new normal was only mildly excruciating. On the other, I felt guilty that I wasn't constantly weeping and suffering at my mother's feet. How could I be so *normal* while watching the woman I cared most about withering away?

But what would weeping and suffering even achieve? Nothing. That's what.

So, I coped. Like everyone else in the world who has ever faced hardship, I learned to bury my scariest emotions down in my chest. And I survived in spite of them.

But then, as always, life had a way of making sure that I never got too comfortable.

It was a quiet night. Mom had just finished watching TV, and I was sitting on my bed in the room I shared with Wayne. Rhondelle had gone to sleep about an hour ago.

Wayne was playing with his trucks on the floor. I always wondered if he thought of Dad when he played with those trucks. I wondered if Wayne hated Dad like I did, or if he simply thought of the man as a strange sort of ghost that drifted in and out of our lives at his own discretion.

Anyway, I missed having my own room. It was nice to have my own space, and my room had a window that overlooked the nice church across the street. Because my room needed to be turned into a spare guest room in case an adult needed to stay over and watch Mom or us kids, I was moved into Wayne's.

Wayne's room wasn't all bad, though. When I looked out *his* window, instead of seeing the church, I could look across the outside corner of our house and see in through *Mom's* bedroom window. This meant that I could pretty much see Mom's room from my bed. I liked that, because I was able to make sure that Mom was okay throughout the night.

Rhondelle used to make fun of me, calling me "nosey." But I wasn't trying to be weird. I was just trying to make sure that our mom was okay. I was a nervous kid, and being able to check in on Mom was as much for her as it was for me.

On that night, I was getting ready to go to bed. My head was already on the pillow, and I was starting to drift off. Wayne was still playing with his trucks, but he was being quiet about it—so I didn't care.

One last time, I decided to peer through the window to check on Mom. When I did, my heart practically stopped.

Mom was convulsing. Badly.

I didn't know what was going on. I didn't even know that convulsions like that meant that someone was having a seizure. But I knew that the erratic way Mom was throwing her body couldn't have been good or natural.

I jumped out of bed, so fast that I was dizzy for two seconds. Then, I ran to her room, just in time to see her fall off of her bed.

Mom's head hit the corner of her wooden nightstand. I feared the worst.

Adrenaline made my heart pound and my brain fuzzy. I didn't run to get Rhondelle or Wayne. There was nothing that they could do to help me. Instead, I grabbed the phone off of Mom's dresser and dialed the only number that I could think of at the time: my Aunt Nina's.

"Nina!" I cried as soon as she picked up. "I need help! Mom is shaking, and she fell on the floor, and she hit her head, and I-,"

"Feisal!" Nina's sharp voice stopped me in my tracks. "Hang up and call 911. I'll be right there."

With my hands trembling, I obeyed. I hung up with Nina and called 911. The operator was friendly, but curt, and soon she was dispatching an ambulance to my house.

The paramedics arrived two minutes before Nina. By the time they'd arrived, Mom had stopped seizing. I'd found my way to her side. I was holding her hand tightly. Even though the immediate convulsions had stopped, Mom wasn't moving or saying anything. She was frozen still, like a living statue.

The paramedics moved swiftly, securing Mom on a stretcher and taking her out of the room. Nina stayed behind with my siblings and me to comfort us. Wayne kept asking questions—and Nina responded to each of them with, "Hush, Wayne. Not now."

The next morning, Nina told all of us what had happened. Mom had suffered a seizure. It had been a pretty severe epileptic episode, and she had been lucky that I'd just so happened to notice her through the window.

Rhondelle had nothing to say about me "nosey" after that.

Nina watched us while Mom was in the hospital.

I remember being relieved about that, because other than Mom, Nina was one of my favorite adults in the world. Like Mom, Nina was caring but fun. She shared my mom's positive attitude and vigor for life, and she was also fiercely protective of her kids. Aunt Nina was like a second mom to me—always there when I needed her, and always trying to protect me.

Nina was heavily moved by God, the church, and the spirit of Christ. She prayed often and talked about God as if he were a friend she knew from grade school, and not an abstraction in the sky. She'd shown me and my cousins a movie called *The Passion of The Christ* when we were kids. The movie was long, and I didn't understand it at the time. I was scared by it, to be perfectly honest. But Aunt Nina cried throughout the entire thing.

I understand now what the film was trying to say— about Jesus Christ dying for the sins of humanity. But would I ever show this to my future kids? Not a chance.

Nina didn't mean to traumatize us kids, though. She just had a gentle spirit and was a great deal more superstitious than almost anyone I knew.

There was this one time I was at Nina's house, and a bird flew in through the window. I was at the kitchen table eating lunch. The bird, probably scared out of its mind, flew into everything. It knocked into lamps, crashed into walls, and screeched like a banshee the entire time. Nina had grabbed a broom and was trying to corral it toward the kitchen window.

The bird flew over my head, and I looked up instinctively.

As soon as I did, the damn thing shitted directly in my left eye.

Instantly, anger filled me. Even as an adult, few things have ever pissed me off quite as much as that stupid bird. I cursed at it, and Nina swatted at it with the broom until it finally left.

Once the bird was out of the house, Nina helped me clean off my eye. She rinsed a rag with water and began wiping my face vigorously.

"It's okay, baby. When a bird poops in your eye, that's good luck."

I know my aunt was only trying to calm me down, but honestly—that was the *last* thing I wanted to hear. As soon as she finished wiping the bird poop off of my face, I raced out of the house and tore down the street—determined to hunt down the bird. Like Liam Neeson hunting down his daughter's kidnappers in *Taken*.

I was probably even muttering his iconic lines in my head as I ran down the street, picking up rocks and chipped pieces of asphalt to use as ammunition. *"I don't know who you are. I don't know what you want. But I will find you and I will kill you."*

I eventually found the winged jerk by the complex dumpsters. I tried throwing my rocks at it, but I kept missing. The bird cooed at me twice as if to rub salt in my wounds, and then fluttered away into a patch of trees across the street.

With my head down, I returned to Nina's house. I tried to remember her consolation—that a bird pooping in your eye was good luck—but I just couldn't bring myself to believe it. Even though I wanted to.

When I got back into the house, Nina had already cleaned up the great mess that the bird had left behind. She'd turned on the radio and was listening to The Temptations. The song was slow and rhythmic, and Nina was nodding her head to it. When she saw me coming through the front door, she waved me over to join her.

I complied, sitting on the couch next to her. I watched her as she nodded her head. Trying to copy her, I began nodding my head as well. But Nina stopped me quickly.

"No, no, baby. Do it like this," Nina said. She made her nods more accented and obvious, showing me how to find the beat of the song even when there wasn't a clear bass drum in it to keep me steady.

To this day, I believe that Nina is the reason I have any rhythm at all.

The day after Mom's seizure, I went to school and told all of my teachers that my mom had overdosed and almost died.

At the time, I had no idea what an *overdose* was. I just knew that it was bad and that it happened to people who took prescription medications. I didn't realize how my claims would come off to my teachers.

I'd heard Nina whispering about it on the phone to some friend of hers, that Mom had suffered an attempted overdose. But *overdosing* seemed to be one of those things that adults didn't need to elaborate on when they talked about it to other adults. So, I didn't know any more than that.

Eventually, one of my teachers pulled me into the hall and told me to stop talking about it.

"Why?" I asked. "It's the truth. She really did overdose."

The teacher's face was grim. "Even so, Feisal. It's not an appropriate school topic."

Even though I couldn't understand my teacher's reasoning as a kid, I registered the serious look on her face, and I realized that this was not a matter of discussion. Putting my head down, I apologized for causing trouble and returned to class.

Now that I'm older, I have the perspective to understand exactly what was happening back then.

Everyone, and I mean *everyone* knew about my mom's illness. My teachers knew, my friends knew, and complete strangers knew. They also knew that Mom was hurting.

They knew in a way that my siblings and I didn't—because Mom never let us see how weak she truly was.

As a kid, I'd thought that Mom's seizure had been random. Now, I know that it probably wasn't.

Mom must have been tired of the pain and suffering that she endured daily. She must have felt like a burden on us, on everybody. She must have decided that the only way to relieve herself was by ending her life.

I'm not angry at Mom for making that choice. In a way, I understood why she did what she did. I don't wish that Mom had made a more responsible decision. I wish that she had better options from the onset.

Eventually, Nina enlisted Grandma to help with us kids.

I don't know how I expected Grandma to act when she came over to visit us at the house, but she was almost scarily nonplussed. I'm sure that inside, she was a swirling storm of emotions. But my family had never excelled at expressing our emotions. She probably thought that it was best to keep a brave face for us kids.

Honestly, we might've needed the opposite. Someone to help us feel our emotions rather than push through them.

Either way, I don't fault Grandma. She was only acting in our best interests.

Grandma didn't live too far away from us. Actually, she was over our house often even before Mom's illness took root. I always liked it when Grandma came over. She was quick to laugh, and her laugh was this unique, contagious thing.

Even if you were in a bad mood, Grandma would find a way to pull the smile out of you.

Despite how much I loved her, I was intimidated by her when I was young. She was independent and well-respected. And like my mom, she had no patience for foolishness. Grandma is the one who kept the family together. She was the picture-perfect image of a model matriarch.

She used to call me "Sal", which were the last three letters of my name. And she used to always do this thing with me—a joke that we'd stolen from Ice Cube's *Friday*. There's this scene where a character named Red tries to get his bike back from the neighborhood bully, Debo. Red brings his father along with him, but Debo manages to force both to leave empty-handed. As Red and his father are leaving, Debo looks at Red's dad and says, "You want some too, old man?"

And Red's father just puts up two fingers and says, "No."

That part always cracked us up. So, every time Grandma saw me, she'd put up her two fingers and say, "Sal, Sal, Sal—no."

When Mom finally came home from the hospital, I almost couldn't bear to see her. Her seizure had done a number on her nervous system. According to Aunt Nina, Mom had lost almost all of her hearing and most of her voice. She couldn't speak to us. She couldn't kiss us goodnight and say "I love you" to us anymore. All she could do was look at us and smile.

And all I could do was try to smile back.

Mom's voice did eventually come back—but it was frail and weaker than before. Almost like a little girl's voice.

Her medical treatment also became much more intense. She went to dialysis multiple times a week for multiple hours at a time. She took her pills dutifully and responsibly.

After some time, she even began to get some strength back. It wasn't enough to walk, but she could lift her arms on her own. And that little thing was enough to give me hope.

With Mom back in the house, a full caretaker needed to be brought in to watch over her. Nina and Grandma helped where they could, but they had their own homes and lives to attend to. That's when Joe moved in.

Joe was a friend from Mom's church. He was a big guy with a stern face and a soft voice. Joe had a son, Benny. We'd been family friends with them for a long time. I'm not sure who asked Joe to help take care of Mom, or why exactly he agreed. All I knew was that Nina and Grandma were grateful that we kids wouldn't have to bear the weight of caretaking with Joe around.

I didn't mind Joe that much. He did everything Mom asked of him without much complaint, and he didn't really impose on our lives. His son, Benny, was a different story.

Benny was older than me by a few years. He was a little moody and sometimes said and did things that I didn't understand. Joe didn't really surveil Benny that much, so Benny got away with all manner of awful things.

But Benny was the price to pay for Joe. And Joe helped Mom.

As I look back on my memories with Mom—both the good and bad—I'm grateful for all the time that I got to spend with her. I'm thankful for the lessons that she taught me simply by virtue of being herself.

She taught me that even though *love* was a four-letter word, it could also be something you said with warm eyes and a big smile. She taught me not to tolerate any foolishness. She taught me to be strong and to appreciate life while I still had a powerful body to enjoy it with.

But mostly, Mom taught me to cherish every moment with the people I love. Because one day, you'll blink and realize that the only thing you have left of them are the memories you made together.

Chapter 9

YVETTE.

*I*t was a beautiful day.

The sun shone brightly, but not oppressively, over the earth. The sky was a clear, pale blue. The kind of blue you only ever see in kid's picture books. There were no clouds in sight. The air was warm and comfortable, and the faint smell of flowers wafted up from the gardens that our neighbors kept.

It was so quiet out that I could hear the choir rehearsing from across the street. I always loved listening to the choir. Their voices bouncing off the high church walls and ceilings made me feel like I was in the center of something pure and beautiful.

The bus slowed to a stop on my street. Rhondelle and I got up, saying goodbye to our friends as we disembarked.

As soon as we got off the bus, I knew something was wrong. Rhondelle knew, too. Her eyebrows were scrunched up.

"Think there's a party going on?" she asked, almost hopeful.

Cars were lined up and down the street. This was usual on Sundays when the church had its weekly service. But today was a Wednesday. There were no services for people to line up around the block for.

"Maybe," I said to Rhondelle, though the sinking feeling in my stomach echoed a different sentiment entirely.

As Rhondelle and I made our way to the house, it quickly became evident that the cars parked up and down the street were those of family and friends. *Our* family and friends. One of my cousins spotted Rhondelle and I walkeing up the sidewalk and rushed over to us. She put her hands on our backs and ushered us up to the front door.

The house was entirely dark except for the sunlight pouring through the windows.

As soon as we stepped through the front door into the living room, Wayne attached himself to my side.

"What's going on?" I asked him.

Wayne just shrugged.

People flooded our house like ants. I saw two of my uncles sitting on the sofa, a handful of older cousins standing against the living room wall in a hushed conference, and familiar strangers loitering around the kitchen.

The truth clicked into my mind almost instantly.

I swallowed thickly before making a break for the stairs leading to the second floor. Wayne and Rhondelle followed after me.

Climbing those stairs felt like climbing Mount Everest. They seemed to stretch on forever. I felt like my legs were made of lead as I forced them to carry me up each step. As my siblings and I emerged upstairs, I began to see the faces of the people who were closest to us. Grandma. Aunt Nina. Uncle Carl.

Everyone's eyes were thick with sadness. And they were all looking at us.

I wanted to scream at them to stop. This was all too much. And it was all confirming my biggest fear. The thing that I had dreaded happening since Mom had first collapsed in her room months ago.

Please, don't let this be real, a little voice in the back of my mind begged. *Please, don't let me be right.*

Part of me wanted to turn tail and run. Maybe if I went back outside and hopped back on the school bus, then I would be able to delay the inevitable. Maybe if I never saw the truth in front of me, I would never be forced to accept it.

Instead, I locked eyes with one of my younger cousins. He'd been crying. His face was splotchy, and his eyes were red-rimmed.

"I'm so sorry," he choked out.

And like that, my suspicions were confirmed.

Aunt Nina smacked his arm and told him to shut his mouth. She said something about *having tact* or whatever. I don't know. I didn't really care. I wasn't mad at my cousin for being the one to break the news to me. In fact, I was glad that it was him. He had always been one of my favorite people. Plus, his voice had been so genuine. I knew how much it must've broken his little heart to have said it.

Rhondelle was already starting to cry behind me because she understood what was happening. And Wayne cried behind her—partially because he understood too, and partially because everyone else around him was crying. I remember being worried for my siblings at that moment. Worried how they'd take the news. How they'd cope with the reality that was quickly and mercilessly hurtling towards us.

I think I clung to that worry a little too hard. I was clinging because it distracted me from the other emotion that I was feeling—pure and utter misery.

None of us wanted to enter Mom's room. But slowly, we managed to put one foot in front of the other.

Grandma was waiting for us in Mom's room. She closed the door behind us so that we could have some privacy away from the rest of the family. In my head, I convinced myself that I was more ready than my siblings to take the news. I stepped forward, looking at Grandma.

Her eyes were awash with hurt, and her voice was hardly greater than a tender whisper.

"Your mama died," she said. I could tell that she'd wanted to say something gentler. Something more eloquent. But those were the only three words that she could manage. She wanted to be strong for us, but she was wrestling with the grief of losing a daughter—a wound that I imagine is just as painful, if not even more so, than that of losing a mother.

I tried to hold back my tears. I failed.

My siblings and I didn't just cry. We *wailed.* Our cries were so loud, that I could hear us setting off a chain reaction of tears down the hallway. Through my stinging tears, I looked at my brother and felt an immense wave of pity for him.

The poor kid was so young. He was just a baby. If he was lucky enough to remember Mom at all, he most likely wouldn't be able to remember the fun times. All the hours of being chased at Fort Fun. All the concessions snacks and rides in her blue Cadillac. He'd have none of it.

The agony of that thought was too much to bear. Grandma tried to comfort me, but I didn't let her. I just took off, running down the stairs and out the front door. I ran down the driveway and onto the sidewalk. I sprinted toward the setting sun, hoping maybe that if I ran fast enough, I'd be able to run right into it. Then, I'd light up like a shooting star, and all the pain in my little body would simply burn away.

I cried. I was miserable. I was angry. And worst of all, I didn't know who I was angry *at*.

Nothing can prepare you to lose a parent. Even though I'd spent the past several months watching Mom decline, even slightly mourning her, there had been a traitorous little flicker of hope in my soul, telling me to believe that she'd get better someday. That the edema and the sickle cell would go away, fading into my memory until it was all just a long-gone nightmare.

My mom was my everything. And I didn't know how to accept the fact that she'd been taken from me.

I wished that I had fought more to see her when she was in the hospital. I wished that I could grab the doctors by their white lab coats and demand that they do everything in their power to save her. I wished that I was closer to God.

Part of me believed that I was being punished. Maybe if I had been more religious—if I had prayed more or if I had actually enjoyed *The Passion of The Christ*—God would have been more merciful with my mom's life.

I was angry at myself for this. And I was angry at Dad for not being there. I didn't know where he was. I hadn't talked to him in weeks.

There was a good chance that he was out on the road with his new family. Not even knowing or caring that his *real* wife—the one that he'd fathered kids with and had promised to love until death—had just fulfilled her end of the deal.

Eventually, I noticed that someone was following behind me. I'd slowed to a walk by then, thoroughly too exhausted to run anymore.

I turned around. The cousin who'd taken me and my siblings to see Mom in the hospital after she'd first collapsed was walking behind me. Apparently, she'd seen me bolt out the door and had decided to come after me. She hadn't wanted to disturb me, knowing that this was just my way of grieving. But she'd wanted to keep an eye on me so that I was safe.

As soon as she saw that I'd noticed her, she quietly closed the distance between us and began walking beside me. We walked in silence for a while. Then, she patted me on the shoulder and said something about going home. I was too tired to argue. We turned around and headed back to the house.

There were only a few people in the house when we returned. My Aunt and Grandma, and a few other close relatives. None of them admonished me for running away. They all seemed to understand why I'd done it, even if I didn't understand it myself.

"Does Dad know?" I asked Aunt Nina.

Nina shook her head. "We tried calling. He didn't answer."

"He's probably busy," Grandma cut in, not wanting to stir in any extra resentment when I was already so emotionally raw. "He'll call back soon, I'm sure. When he does, I'll make sure you talk to him."

I was doubtful of Grandma's claim. And after several days, my doubts were proven to be correct.

Dad never called to offer his condolences.

Not once.

Chapter 10

BAG OF JEWELS

T he next several days were a blur.

Family and friends and even complete strangers came in and out of our house throughout the day. They barely talked to Rhondelle, Wayne, or me. Usually, they just tried (and failed) to look us in the eyes while uttering a half-hearted "sorry for your loss." Nobody wanted to face the sorry kids that had just lost their mother.

Especially since the reason they'd come had been anything but noble.

The visitors treated my mom's house like it was a free-for-all. A garage sale with a 100% discount. I seethed as they rummaged through Mom's stuff, taking it by the armful to their cars without so much as asking.

I saw them walking out with Mom's jackets, scarves, shoes, and anything else that could be carried with two hands.

The anger that I felt towards these people was sharp and brittle. Most of them had not been around at all to help when Mom had been sick. Fewer still had ever called to check in. To be honest, I don't even remember a lot of the people being around when Mom was *healthy*. And yet, they thought that they were entitled to Mom's things. As if knowing someone's first name and address was all that was necessary to be written into their will.

And I guess it was because nobody tried to stop them.

A handful of my aunts—aunts who had never been as close to Mom as Aunt Nina was—welcomed people into our house. They invited those who came to take as much as they wanted. I think they figured that the more people took, the less there would be for them to have to deal with. For as much as I loved my aunts, it killed me to know that they were allowing these strangers to steal the little bits and pieces of Mom that I still had.

Nobody thought to save any of Mom's stuff for Wayne, Rhondelle, or me. Least of all, us. I guess when you're a kid, you don't just start grabbing things for yourself because you're expecting someone else to do it for you. Or you don't want to get in trouble for taking things that aren't yours.

Even though Rhondelle didn't fit into any of Mom's clothes at the time, I'm sure that it would've been nice for her to have some of them. Hell, I would've been happy taking a hat or a shirt—if not to wear, then to keep as a memento.

At one point, Rhondelle, Wayne, and I were hanging out in my room. We'd all grown tired of the adults coming in and out of the house and wanted to hide away for a while until things died down.

A knock came at the door, and Aunt Nina let herself in. She looked just as exhausted as we were. Maybe even more so.

"Don't tell them I said this, but your aunties have lost their damn minds," Nina huffed. "Letting any old fool off the street come in and take your mama's things. I think one of them even made out with your daddy's machete."

My eyes widened. Dad's machete was one of his favorite things. It was huge. Mom and Dad kept it in Mom's coat closet, behind all the coats. They absolutely forbade us kids from even so much as looking at it. How someone had managed to walk out with one of Dad's things—a giant sword, no less—was beyond me.

"Did they take the masks?" I asked.

Mom had three porcelain masks that she hung up for decoration. They were all white, with different colored ribbons running through them. I always wanted to take one of them off the wall to wear. I didn't dare do it, though, because I knew that my clumsy ass would probably end up breaking it.

Still, I really wanted to keep them. They were cool.

Nina shook her head. "Sorry, Feisal," was all she said. "Like I said, your aunties have lost their minds."

Nina didn't usually talk about adult things with us kids. But she must've been too frustrated to even bother this time.

I was thankful for it. It was nice to know that there was at least one adult in the house not actively condoning this madness.

Nina had argued for days with her sisters about the strangers that they were letting into the house. I'd heard them going at it in the kitchen late at night when they thought we kids were asleep. Nina tried her hardest to protect Mom's things, but at the end of the day, she couldn't claim a greater right to Mom's stuff than they could.

"Hey," Nina said, reaching into her coat. "Don't look so down. Especially you, Rhondelle."

Rhondelle tilted her head.

Nina smiled, pulling out a small bag of Mom's jewelry. My eyes widened as I saw the hoop earrings that I'd always loved glinting in the bottom of the bag. "I managed to sneak these out for you three. Your mom would want you to have these, so keep them safe, okay?"

I felt my heart welling up with gratitude.

We agreed that Rhondelle would hold on to the bag.

It was a little thing, but it lifted my spirits greatly.

Looking back on it now, I realize that giving Mom's stuff away was about as easy on my aunts as it would've been on anyone. They didn't want to give away Mom's things either. But they had to.

At the time, I didn't think about where Mom's stuff would have to go if they didn't allow people to take things. I didn't think about how much stuff they'd be responsible for storing. I didn't realize that most of Mom's things would probably find their way to Goodwill anyway. All I saw was a bunch of vultures taking my mom's belongings right after she'd passed away.

Chapter 11

THE DRIVE OF NO RETURN

As we drove down the highway toward Arkansas, it felt as though my stomach couldn't stop doing somersaults.

After a few weeks of waiting for Dad to call, I eventually got fed up with his radio silence and called him. When Dad picked up, I unloaded everything on him. I told him about Mom's death, about the vultures that had taken her things, and about how sad and lonely my siblings and I were.

"Can you please come pick us up?" I asked, out of breath from relaying everything. "We want to come and live with you, Dad."

I guess some little part of me was hoping that Mom's death might be able to bring us together or something.

Dad paused for a moment. Then, he said, "Yeah, man. I'll come get y'all. Have your stuff ready, okay?"

"Okay."

I hung up the phone. Then I went upstairs to tell Wayne and Rhondelle the news—we were going to be living with Dad from now on. I didn't tell anybody that I had specifically called Dad and asked him to get us. I didn't ask for my siblings' input on the move. I just assumed that they wanted out of Mom's old house as much as I did.

I guess that I was being selfish.

But I was a kid. And Mom's death had broken me in a major way. Now that our mom was gone, it felt like nobody in the world could relate to my siblings and me. Our friends treated us like outsiders. Like we'd shatter into a million pieces if they so much as dared to say the "m" word. And the thing was, we probably would have.

At the time, I thought living with our dad would be the best decision for all of us.

Little did I know at the time, but that would go on to be one of the decisions that changed my life forever. And not in a good way.

The drive was ghostly quiet. It didn't feel like a family road trip. It didn't feel like we were headed to a better place. It felt more like a death march across state lines.

At times, the radio would be on, humming out R&B hits. At other times, the car would be completely silent save for the growl of the engine and a few snores from my siblings.

I couldn't fully fall asleep in the car. I nodded off a few times, but never for more than a couple of minutes. My trust issues kept me from dozing completely.

Had it only been Dad and my siblings in the car, I might've been able to rest. But there was someone else there—a woman sitting in the passenger's seat.

I recognized her the instant I saw her.

My siblings and I had met her months ago. Mom had hesitantly allowed us to take a trip up to see Dad in Arkansas for a few nights. It was wintertime and it was so cold that icicles the size of my entire body were dangling precariously from every rooftop.

We rode bikes during the day. And at night, we played games in the guest room.

Dad's girlfriend, Kalisha, had two kids: Cal and Maya. They were rowdier than us. However, the game that we were playing had us all worked up equally.

I guess we were being too noisy because, at some point in the middle of the game, Kalisha stomped up to the room and began screaming her head off at us. She told us to shut up, and that if we kept being loud, she'd be giving all of us a "Whoopin'".

My siblings and I went dead silent. We were stunned. We'd all been scolded, of course, but never in our lives had we been admonished so severely for something so small. Regardless, none of us wanted to get in trouble.

Except Cal and Maya apparently didn't get the memo.

They kept being noisy—yelling and arguing and even pushing each other. They tried to get Wayne, Rhondelle, and

95

me in on it. Wayne could be convinced, but Rhondelle and I stayed quiet. As I watched the noise level rise, a spike of anxiety pierced my stomach. I tried to distance myself from the others. I wanted nothing to do with them or their game should Kalisha come back into the room to make good on her threat.

Being in that house was like sitting under a dark cloud just waiting for the thunder and lightning to strike.

And now, I realized with a sinking sensation, that was going to be our lives permanently.

Maybe she'd just been in a bad mood that night. Maybe she wasn't normally like that, I tried to reason with myself. But I knew that I was wrong. There was a feeling in the pit of my gut telling me that things were not going to be okay. And I was inclined to believe it.

As I sat in the car, half-dazed and staring out the window at the semi-green Arkansas landscape, I wondered if I had made a mistake calling Dad. A little worrying voice in the back of my head whispered premonitions of something awful. Something worse than being cooped up under the same roof that my mom had died under. Something worse than being taken care of by a collection of loosely obligated adults.

But I pushed it away.

I forced myself to be optimistic. Even if that meant blinding myself temporarily to the truth.

Chapter 12

FAÇADE SWEET FAÇADE

*A*fter arriving in Arkansas, we pulled up to a huge house on a road called Chester Street. As a ten-year-old, I thought the house looked like a mansion. It was big and blue, with red bricks lining the front façade and a striking red roof. It had multiple entrances. There were two doors leading into the house from the front. Both looked like they could be the main door.

This house could have eaten my mom's house for breakfast.

Dad parked the car and opened up the trunk for us to grab our suitcases. We made our way up to the house, our eyes drinking it in and trying to feel out what it would be like to call this place *our home.*

Kalisha and Dad gave us a quick tour of the space.

Walking in the main front door (which I found out was the one closer to the driveway), we were met with an empty family room space. The family room featured a fireplace but very little actual furniture. A den sat off to the right, and further up and to the left was a formal dining room. A laundry room tucked itself away in the hall. Past that, another door offered access to the other half of the house.

Through there, you could find Dad and Kalisha's room. And then, further down, the kitchen and what appeared to be *another* living room. A side door led to the backyard. A set of stairs went down to the basement. And finally, a second hallway took you to two more bedrooms and a bathroom.

Later on, as I'd explore more of the neighborhood, I'd be amazed at how different Arkansas was from Virginia. The neighborhood was small, with houses all ranging in size and grandeur. A couple of kids lived on our block, but not many. But strangest of all, the street was quiet. There were no kids playing basketball. No cars parked up and down the street every Sunday. No choir rehearsals. Just silence.

We only lived on Chester Street for a few years. But the years were long.

Nothing in that house was ever normal. Nothing felt familiar to the cozy, loving upbringing that Mom had worked so hard to give us. It always felt like something horrible was happening. And if something horrible *wasn't* happening, then it was *going to happen* soon.

One of the immediate issues was the sheer occupancy of the house.

With Dad, Kalisha, my siblings and I, and Kalisha's two kids, there were seven people total crammed into a house with three bedrooms.

Kalisha's kids were roughly the same age as my siblings and me. I was the oldest out of all of us. Rhondelle was next. Then Cal and Maya. And finally, Wayne was the youngest.

I had mixed feelings about Kalisha's kids. Maya was fine. I didn't really talk to her that much. We were pretty far apart in age, and with us being opposite genders, there wasn't much for us to relate to with one another.

Cal was a different story. He was brash and outgoing. Even though he was younger than me, he acted like he was older.

At the school that we all went to, I'd occasionally see him acting like a fool with a bunch of other kids, demanding to be the center of attention. Cal was similar to my father in that people generally liked him. His confidence and lack of deference earned him respect among the boys, and his charm bought him points with the girls.

Cal seemed to be dating a new girl every few weeks. I remember him nudging me with his elbow, always eager to casually brag about the latest pretty thing he'd have vying for his attention.

At home, he hogged the TV and exclusively watched anime. His favorite show was Dragon Ball Z. Even though I didn't care for the show myself, I often found myself passing the time by watching them with him. We'd sit in the living room, tracing the characters on paper and cutting them out to craft makeshift action figures.

The action figures never looked very good, and often got crumpled up a few days into play. But I always thought that they were creative—and useful considering we didn't have many plastic toys other than the standard army men and superheroes.

Despite this case of amicable behavior, Cal and I never really got on. As the eldest sons of our respective clans, we were both hungry to claim the role of *alpha male* amongst the kids. Rhondelle and Wayne loved me. And Maya idolized Cal. And we were all a little at odds with one another.

I expected this to be the case when I'd signed on to live with Dad and Kalisha. What I didn't expect was for the *adults* in the house to pick a side as well.

It sounds a bit silly to say—especially since Cal wasn't even in the double-digits at the time—but he held a lot of power in our house. Whatever he said, went. And he wasn't shy about using this privilege, either. Dad and Kalisha treated Cal like *he* was the one paying the rent. They bent over backward to please him, like his own personal constituents.

It bugged me for a number of reasons. First, because I had never known my father to bend to *anyone's* will—not to mention the will of a child. Second, it became immediately evident that Dad *favored* Kalisha's kids over my siblings and me.

I'd known that the days of Dad and I fishing together were gone (even if the stupidest part of me hoped for the longest time that we'd somehow reignite that bond again). But I thought that we'd had some kind of comradery. We were bound by blood. He was my father. I was his son. I thought that would be enough.

Apparently not.

In the years that he'd been seeing Kalisha behind Mom's back, he'd also taken on a fathering role toward her kids. Arguably, he was more of a father to Cal and Maya than he ever was to my siblings or me. I'd be lying if I said I wasn't angry. While Mom was fighting a losing battle against her sickle cell, Dad was playing house with this woman and her kids.

I resented Cal a little for it. But I mainly disliked him by principal of our differing personalities.

Rhondelle never bickered with Maya. I don't think either of them had bad blood against the other. Wayne made a concentrated effort to get along with Cal. He realized better than I did that appeasing Cal offered the best chance at survival in our new house.

I wasn't in the business of appealing to Cal's sensibilities, though. Mostly, I just tried to stay out of his way. And thankfully, he did the same for me.

When we first moved to Arkansas, Dad was around quite a bit. I almost foolishly believed that things would change for the better between us. As if the only thing keeping him from being the father that I knew and loved was a little bit of distance.

But before I knew it, he was on the road again.

He'd be gone for weeks. Sometimes even for more than a month. And we would all be left to fend for ourselves.

Technically, Kalisha watched us. But her approach to caregiving started and stopped at ensuring that none of us died of starvation. She took on a detached role—hardly ever even speaking to my siblings or me unless we came to her first. I had a feeling that she disliked our presence in the house. Maybe she felt that we were somehow encroaching on her life. Messing up the perfect little family unit that she had built with our father.

Oh, the irony.

To her credit, she was kind to her own children. And she was nice to Wayne.

Kalisha also did what she felt was necessary to keep order in the home. She was strict about everything—from bedtime curfews to when and how we should play with one another. Wayne often got in trouble for his tendency to play alone.

He'd be quietly playing with his trucks as he always did, and then Cal would come bursting in to ask if Wayne would let him borrow a truck. Wayne's trucks were his prized possessions, so he usually declined. Then, Cal would go to Kalisha to complain. Kalisha would force Wayne to share his trucks with Cal. This happened so many times that eventually, Wayne wizened up to the reality of the situation:

unless he wanted to get in trouble, he needed to share. Not only toys but also space and time.

We were all a little unused to the near militaristic strictness with which Kalisha ran the household. Back in Virginia, the rules had been lax. We had to be respectful. And we had to listen if Mom ever told us to knock it off. But general, our baseline for good behavior involved doing homework on time, not harming ourselves, and not harming others.

Here, there were a lot more rules. My siblings and I learned them quickly, though. We didn't really have any other choice.

Inevitably, though, Dad *would* come home from his job on the road. And when that happened, we'd all be graced with about five precious minutes of normality. Dad would come through the door, the sound of his boots kicking against the doorframe signaling his arrival. He'd give us all a round of hugs and hellos. Then, he would mutter something about being tired and steal away into his room. He wouldn't come out after that, except for one of two reasons: to grab a bite from the kitchen or to reprimand one of us kids.

I could always tell when Dad was walking around. His footsteps were loud as if he was trying with every step to communicate his own oppressive presence.

Soon, I grew to fear those footsteps.

Part of it was the lack of predictability. You never knew whether Dad was coming out to eat or to yell. Kalisha would keep a mental track record of everything that had gone wrong during the week—whether one of us had gotten a bad grade on a homework assignment, whether we'd mouthed off to her, or anything else. Then, when Dad came home, she'd unload all of it on him so that he could handle it.

I never did get comfortable living in that house. It never felt *right*. It was like a puzzle piece—the kind that looks like it should fit in an empty space, but when you try to jam it in, you realize that one of the lines doesn't quite match up with the pieces around it.

Still, I forced myself to make it work.

This house was my new life. These people were my new family. Refusing to accept that was a fool's game. Sure, things were different, but did that have to mean that they'd be bad? Maybe all I needed was a bit of perspective and some forced positivity.

My resolve lasted for about a month.

As my life tended to go, things quickly started to run south.

Chapter 13

SLAP OF AUTHORITY

*A*fter a few weeks, I'd acclimated myself to my new world. I was making friends at school, staying on my best behavior at home, and trying my hardest to get along with my new family. I couldn't say that I felt happy, but I wasn't exactly miserable either. I was more or less in an emotional state of purgatory.

This felt laughably *okay* compared to how my life had been months ago.

Looking back, I'm proud of myself for how hard I tried to make the best of a bad situation. There was nothing else I could have done to make my life less terrible. Like with Mom and her illness, I don't blame myself for not making better choices. I just wish that I had gotten better options.

Cal, Wayne, and I were playing action figures the first time it happened.

We were in one of the living spaces, our paper cutouts held carefully in our hands as we pretended to shoot energy blasts at one another. Just like in the anime shows that Cal watched, we yelled at the top of our lungs as we declared the names of each attack.

I guess we were being too loud. Kalisha stormed into the room; a scowl etched on her face.

"Don't y'all know how to act in a house?" Kalisha yelled. I couldn't help but notice that she was only looking at Wayne and me. "Watch the noise, fuck."

As she left, I heard her mutter something under her breath about *"Jamal and his damn kids."*

The *damn kids* in question referring to my brother and me.

As soon as Kalisha was out of the room, Cal rolled his eyes and convinced us to keep playing. When I told him that I didn't want to play anymore because I didn't want to get his mom Mad, Cal just rolled his eyes.

"She's just being stupid," Cal said. "Come on. Play."

Wayne and I reluctantly rejoined the game, though both of us were sure to keep our voices down. Cal, however, was apparently taking his mother's warning as a challenge. He yelled like a crazy person, seemingly trying to egg us on into yelling with him.

Unsurprisingly, it didn't take long for Kalisha to come stomping back into the room.

"What the fuck did I just say?" She demanded. Her face was twisted into a rage.

Cal shrugged. "Sorry, Mama. I tried to tell them to be quieter, but they wouldn't listen."

It took me a second to register what he was saying. He tried to tell *us* to be quiet?! Was he really trying to pass that phony lie off as the truth? I almost couldn't believe it. There was no way Kalisha would take Cal's word for it. Not when she could literally *hear* that he was the one who'd been yelling.

I was so certain of this truth that I didn't even think to say a word in my defense.

In retrospect, I probably should have. Not that it would've changed anything—but maybe I would've been able to enjoy a bit more dignity after what came next.

Kalisha marched over to me, snatching me up by the arm. Her fingers closed around me like a vice, her nails digging into the soft flesh of my forearm. I'd never been grabbed like that in all my life. I didn't know what to do. I thought that she was just going to yell again.

But she didn't.

Kalisha reeled back, pulling her free hand high above her head before bringing it down against my face.

I didn't cry out in pain. I just fell to my butt in shock. My fingers drifted up to the stinging spot on my cheek. I was in disbelief.

Mom had never hit us. And under her watch, neither had Dad.

To be smacked by this woman—this stranger who I hardly even knew—felt like an insult. And yet, there was

107

nothing that I could do to retaliate. Before I could even get my bearings, Kalisha snapped at us to be quiet again and then retreated to whatever she'd been doing before we'd interrupted her with our noise.

Once I'd finally pulled myself back together, I glared at Cal.

"Why did you lie?" I demanded. "I wasn't being loud, and you know it."

"Yes, you were," Cal said, shrugging. He seemed completely nonplussed over the whole situation. He'd tricked his own mother into smacking the hell out of me, and he didn't even have the guts to look guilty about it.

I tried accusing him of lying again. But Cal just brushed me off and called me a "punk" for getting so worked up.

Cal asked Wayne and me to play again, but we refused—neither of us wanting to risk facing Kalisha's wrath again. Part of me worried that Cal would go running to his mom to complain about us not playing with him, as he often did whenever we refused to join in on his "fun." But thankfully, he didn't.

He called us boring. Then, he left to go play on his own in our shared room.

Wayne asked me quietly if I was okay. Realizing that I was still cradling my cheek, I retracted my hands from my face and nodded.

"Yes," I lied. "I'm good."

And thankfully, Wayne was satisfied by that answer.

Chapter 14

DREAMING OF AN ANGEL

*I*n my dreams, Mom was still alive.

And not only was she alive, but she was also *healthy.* Her sickle cell had receded, leaving her young and jubilant, and just as I remembered her being in all of my happiest memories.

In my dreams, Mom drove to Chester Street. She climbed up the stairs leading to our front door and knocked like a SWAT agent conducting a raid.

Kalisha answered the door, but Mom didn't even acknowledge her. She just barged right into the house and started calling for Wayne, Rhondelle, and me.

We ran to her, our faces joyful and full of relief. Our feet felt light as we leaped into her arms.

In my dreams, Mom carried all three of us out the door of that house and to her perfect, undamaged blue Cadillac. She buckled us into the backseat and told us how happy she was to see us again. We echoed back the sentiment.

In my dreams, Mom drove us back to Virginia. Back to her little house, where Aunt Nina and Grandma were waiting for us. We moved back into our rooms, where all of our stuff had magically been replaced and put back just how we'd left it. Mom would take us to Fort Fun to run around while the sun was still out. And when it started to get dark and cold, Mom would sweep us back into the house and we'd watch scary movies until keeping our eyes open felt like a chore.

In my dreams, Mom tucked us back into our beds. She told each of us goodnight individually. She told us that she loved us.

And in my dreams, I finally said it back.

Chapter 15

A Fist To The Chest

*I*t was no secret that Cal got on my nerves.

As mentioned before, I was mostly indifferent toward my new stepsiblings. Deep down, I knew that they hadn't asked to share a space with us any more than we had asked to share a space with them. I wanted to be amicable toward them. I tried hard to get along with Kalisha's kids. I tried to convince myself that they weren't the ones at fault—Kalisha and Dad were. But exhibiting that kind of grace is hard when you're a kid.

Maya was like a ghost to me. Sometimes there, sometimes not. But she never really bothered me. She mostly kept to her room. And she was young enough that our paths didn't cross in school.

Cal, though, was harder to avoid. We were only a grade apart, which meant that there was a lot more crossover in our lives. The people that we knew tended to know each other. And that meant that essentially, we were competing for attention and love from the same pool of friends.

I wasn't as outspoken as Cal. But I was liked regardless. Maybe even *because* I wasn't as outspoken as him. Either way, he was jealous. Sometimes, I'd catch him across the courtyard, glaring at me as I talked with my new friends. I tried not to pay attention to him. Lord knows Cal didn't need any more attention.

Despite being a year younger than me, Cal was convinced that he was smarter. And Kalisha and Dad held the same belief. In fact, it got to a point where it almost felt that I wasn't *allowed* to be smarter than Cal.

I remember afternoons spent at home, working on homework quietly with my siblings and stepsiblings. I always breezed through homework, but with Cal around, I had to slow my pace. I couldn't look too bright. Anything that threatened Cal's place as the crown jewel of the family was strictly forbidden—if not explicitly, then implicitly.

Sometimes, Cal and I would ask each other for help on assignments. Usually, I would ask Cal directly if I needed help. But if Cal had to ask me, he'd do so in a roundabout sort of way because he didn't want me to know that he didn't understand something.

Instead of just asking anything directly, he'd make a statement and wait for me to correct him on it. And then, if and when I corrected him, he'd nod thoughtfully and say something like, "Yeah, that's basically what I said, too."

And I'd try like hell not to roll my eyes because if I did, he'd go crying to Kalisha that I was giving him an attitude "for no reason."

It soon became obvious that Cal didn't want us around. He didn't like that Wayne and I threatened his role as "man of the house." And he didn't like Rhondelle because he claimed that she was "a snob." Really, he was just upset that she'd turned down his few attempts at flirting with her.

Still, I'd tolerated bratty kids like Cal before. I'd dealt with my fair share of Cals in school. The problem that I was starting to run into regarding my stepbrother wasn't so much *him* as it was how Dad and Kalisha *treated him*.

The favoritism was glaring. Like spilled wine on a white carpet.

Cal (and Maya, to an extent) were practically untouchable when it came to punishments. Whenever Kalisha came to yell at us, she always made sure to direct her ire at Wayne, Rhondelle, or me. She would have let Cal and Maya get away with murder if they so pleased.

And Cal often ran with this. He'd purposefully do things to get me in trouble. He'd lie and say that I'd called him a name when I didn't. And Kalisha would eat up his words every time. For the longest time, I hated Cal for this fact. But with age and wisdom, I came to realize that Cal was just acting as any child in his position probably would have. In his eyes, we were intruders. Kids shipped in from Dad's past marriage to wreak havoc upon the lives of his sister, his mother, and most importantly—himself.

Cal's tattling was probably how he felt he could take control of the situation. It was a little way of getting back at me—the guy who had stolen his rightful throne as the oldest male child in the house.

I almost wanted to understand him.

Almost.

There was a part of me that was angry and vindictive. And this part wanted nothing more than to see Cal get a taste of his own medicine. I downright *fantasized* about how Dad would punish Cal if he were home to see everything happening for himself. I imagined Kalisha stepping back to allow Dad to dole out rightful judgment upon my stepbrother. I imagined Dad's swift punishments to be fair. Or, at least fairer than Kalisha's were.

Unfortunately, those fantasies were soon to be dashed. Obliterated into a million tiny pieces, never to recover.

It was late, and I was half awake, half-asleep in bed. Sharing a bedroom with Cal and Wayne meant that it was hard for me to get to sleep on some nights. I didn't mind sharing space with Wayne, but I still didn't trust Cal entirely.

Without warning, the door was thrown open. Light from the hallway poured into our bedroom, right into my eyes.

"Who the fuck is creeping around my house?" Dad's voice boomed. "I know y'all ain't really sleeping. Get the fuck up!"

My eyes opened, squinting reflexively from the light. I could hear Wayne and Cal stirring as well.

Dad kept yelling at us until I was sure that the whole house—no, the whole *neighborhood*—had been woken up as well. His voice was rising in volume and intensity. It was clear that this wasn't one of his regular admonishments. For some reason, Dad was *fuming.*

If Mom were here, she'd set Dad straight in an instant. She'd tell him that he sounded like a ridiculous fool yelling his head off at a bunch of kids. But Mom wasn't here. It was just us three kids.

And none of us dared to criticize Dad.

"Well?" Dad demanded.

I looked at Wayne and Cal, trying to see if either of them knew anything about what was going on. Both seemed as confused as I was.

Finally, Cal spoke up. "I think I saw Feisal walking around."

My jaw dropped. I stared at Cal, wide-eyed. He didn't meet my gaze.

"No, I wasn't!" I asserted.

Cal furrowed his brow. "No, I definitely remember you walking around. You woke me up for a second."

He sounded so earnest that he almost fooled me. And I was the one that he was accusing!

Did I get up to pee or something? I wondered, doubting my own memory. I shook my head. No, I definitely didn't get up to pee. I'd been in my bed all night. Just like Wayne and Cal. So, why was Dad looking at me like I was guilty of something?

"I did not," I said, more confidently. I looked at Dad, trying to channel all the sincerity I could muster up into my expression, "Dad, I swear. I was asleep."

Dad didn't seem to care that I was telling him the truth. He didn't seem to care that I was begging him with my eyes, *please believe me.* He didn't seem to care about anything but taking out his own anger on someone.

And that someone was me.

Without another word, Dad walked over to me. Then, he punched me in the chest.

The punch was hard. And I hadn't been braced for it. I gasped as his fist slammed against my small body. In one swift hit, he'd knocked the wind right out of me. Wayne yelped. I choked. Dad huffed. As I lay back against my mattress, clutching my dully aching chest, it felt as though I'd just walked up a hundred flights of stairs.

After punching me, Dad turned around. "Now take your ass to bed," he said. His voice was more even than it had been moments ago. As if he'd somehow taken all of his anger and channeled it right into that painful blow.

He slammed the door shut, leaving all of us in darkness.

My body throbbing with pain, I didn't even care that Cal had (yet again) gotten me in trouble. I just felt betrayed. My own father, the man to whom I owed my flesh and blood, had taken Cal's word over mine.

I cried myself to sleep that night. Although I made sure to be quiet. I didn't want the noise of my sobs to anger Dad a second time.

It was that night that I was hit with the hard truth: Dad and I had just crossed the point of no return. No matter what either of us did—things from now on would never be the same as they once were.

The morning after, I was in a haze. If not for the burgeoning bruise on my chest, I might not have even believed that the events of the night previous had happened. As I washed my face and gently poked the sore flesh, I ran through the haunting scene over and over again in my head.

Was there something that I could've done differently? Should I have put up a better defense for myself? Should I have turned the blame on Cal? Maybe I'd been sitting a certain way on the bed. Maybe I was too slow to answer, and that made me look guilty.

I didn't know. I still don't know. I probably never will.

I never confronted Cal about the lie that he'd told. Even though I wanted to, I knew that it would do me no good. Worse, it might even reignite Dad's anger and bring it back for a repeat performance.

I tried to give Dad the benefit of the doubt. Maybe he believed Cal because he'd spent more time with him over the past few years than he had with me. Maybe he truly did think that I was the guilty party and wasn't just acting on blind suggestion.

Walking down to the kitchen to eat breakfast before school, I wondered if my dad would apologize to me.

But Dad didn't even look up to greet me when I sat down at the table. He didn't say sorry.

And soon, I realized that it was foolish of me to have ever expected him to.

Chapter 16

MEMPHIS

The days after I'd been punched were uneventful. In fact, I might even go as far as to say that they were *peaceful*.

To the best of my memory, nobody got in trouble. Nobody fought or bickered. Other than the ache in my chest and the weird splotch of purple discoloration below my sternum, everything was shockingly good.

Cal must've felt a little bad about putting me in Dad's line of fire because he took care to avoid me. And even though Dad didn't apologize, he didn't get angry again for the rest of the week.

To me, it was starting to appear as though some demon had momentarily possessed him—but that the demon had now been exorcised. Maybe he had even been exorcised *through* the punch.

Either way, I was grateful.

Time passed, and my bruise eventually faded away until all that was left of it was the faint recollection of the blow that had caused it.

The drive to Memphis was long but nice.

Dad had elected to take me with him on the road. I don't know what inspired him to take me, but I was glad to join him. Despite my mixed feelings towards Dad in general these days, I'd always wanted to drive in his truck with him.

One thing that I will say about my father is that he took work seriously. He was proud of his job as an international truck driver. He was happy that his work helped to keep the world running. My dad was no desk jockey.

Dad's trucks were also nice. They were huge and shiny. As we drove down the highway, I imagined all the other drivers in their little sedans envying the size and power of our ride.

As a driver, Dad's main job was helping people move. He'd load up all their things into his truck, and then drive to wherever their new house was—whether it was a few states away or on the other side of the country.

At the time, I didn't really understand *why* Dad had chosen this job. It didn't really seem fun hauling people's things across the country. But I still respected the fact that Dad knew how to hustle for a living. Plus, being on the road with him felt like a nice deviation from my everyday kid life in his and Kalisha's house.

Unlike Kalisha, Dad was extremely lenient with what I did (so long as nothing I did interrupted his ability to work). I could sleep in the truck, stay up all night if I wanted, and eat anytime I wanted. And the food that I ate was always junky. McDonald's, and gas station Hot Cheetos, and soda. The kind of stuff that kids die for and that mothers hate.

Dad was also much more enjoyable to be around when he was on the road. He wasn't strict at all. Most of the time he liked to sit back quietly and drive. But sometimes, he'd be willing to talk or joke around. On the road, Dad became a strange phantom of himself. Or at least the man he used to be.

"You see, his mom was a Baptist, and his dad was something else. Methodist, I think. Anyways, it doesn't matter, because the guy didn't really believe in either of them..." Dad was currently on the topic of Muhammed Ali's spiritualism. I didn't know how we'd gotten to the subject, but Dad seemed to want me to absorb every word that he was telling me. "And so, he was at this tournament. And he met this guy who worked for the Islamic church or something like that. And that changed his life."

"Why Islam?" I asked. I tried to keep my voice as neutral as possible. Even when Dad wasn't in a bad mood, I had to police myself around him.

Dad waved a finger. "Because he believed that it was the rightful religion of Black people. But either way, God was in his heart. You remember that. No matter what religion you choose, keep Him in your heart."

I nodded, studying Dad's words like he was a lecturer at a university.

At the time, I knew that Dad was struggling with a lot. I don't exactly know what, although I have my suspicions. I think religion—or at least, *thinking* about religion—helped him cope with it.

122

Islam had been a part of his life since he was a child. His parents had become converts of the Islamic faith shortly after his birth. Dad had always quietly followed the faith, but lately his interest in the religion was increasing and becoming more overt. But even so, he never forced his religion upon Wayne, Rhondelle, or me, which I was grateful for.

I wish that I'd been able to help Dad back then. I wish that it wasn't just the teachings of Islam that supported him when he was at his lowest. It was clear that he felt the entire world was on his shoulders. The pressures of life seemed to weigh greatly on him.

He was, after all, the only one paying any bills. And now that I had called him and unceremoniously saddled him with three more mouths to feed, that bill was only getting higher.

As we continued down the interstate highway toward Memphis, I found myself again clinging to this strange sense of normalcy between my father and me. The night that he'd punched me had been pushed into the recesses of my mind, shoved into a dark corner like an old box of inherited antiques. This road trip could mark a new beginning. It could be the catalyst for betterment.

At the very least, it could be a promise that things would not get worse.

That night, as the stars streaked above us and the headlights of Dad's truck carved a path through the velvet night, I prayed. I wasn't sure who to pray to—the Christian

God or the Muslim God. I just sent my words up into the heavens.

Please. Help my father. Make things alright again. I drew a quick cross across my chest with my finger. *I'm putting my faith in you, God. Amen.*

Chapter 17

"DAD. I SWEAR, I DIDN'T"

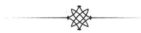

*G*od did not in fact hear my prayers. Or, if He did, He ignored them. I imagined him up in some cloud-filled palace, his white robes flowing and magnificent, as he checked some heavenly version of his email.

I could picture him clicking on my prayer—my email—and opening it. Bored as he scanned through it with his all-knowing eyes. Then, he'd right-click my email and mark it as *low priority.* He'd file it away in his "respond to later" folder as he went back to answering the prayers of movie stars and millionaires and all the people who already had it all.

He'd notice a new email at the top of his inbox with the subject line, **PRAYER REQUEST FROM KIM KARDASHIAN: A NEW MAKEUP LINE PRETTY PLEASE,** tilt his head back, and exclaim, "Finally! Something interesting."

Okay, maybe that mental image is a little sacrilegious. In truth, I'm sure God had a plan for me. I just sometimes wish that his plan didn't involve so much suffering on my end.

After returning home from Memphis, things at the house slowly but surely slipped back into their usual rhythm. Cal was back to being a brat. Kalisha was back to being a jerk. And Dad was back to his moody, unpredictable self.

It was like being in the home reminded him of the fact that he was burdened with dependents. Dependents that he did not want. That he did not even particularly care for.

All too soon, the punching incident would come back to me.

Dad was home for a day or two. Then, he was back on the road for two months. My siblings and I went about our daily rituals. School, homework, trying not to piss off Kalisha, repeat. The house was a little tense as it always was, but nothing too egregious.

But then Dad came back.

I didn't know how to feel about Dad's return. On the one hand, I was happy to see him. I was happy that he'd come back at all. Sometimes I worried that he'd jump ship all over again and start yet another family with another woman and leave us all behind. It was relieving to see him trudge through the front doors of our Chester Street house.

But there were other parts of me that weren't so happy.

Because when Dad was home, that was when the *true* punishments were doled out. And usually, regardless of who had committed the infraction, it was me or my siblings taking the heat for it.

For example, one of Dad's biggest grievances was socks left on the floor. It sounds so stupid and trivial when I write it out like that. But that was the truth.

In a traditional home, socks on the floor were a nuisance at best. Maybe your mom would yell at you for your untidiness before unceremoniously chucking the sock into your laundry basket. If she was in a bad mood and you were a repeat offender, she might even give you a little grounding to really drive the point home. But ultimately, that would be that.

In my house, however, a sock on the floor was equivalent to stealing from the liquor store.

I can't remember what the sock looked like. I can only remember Dad's face as he angrily held it up in front of us kids and demanded to know whose it was.

None of us answered. We never did.

The sock was mostly black with a patch of gray on the toes. That meant that it could've been Wayne's, Cal's, or mine.

Dad shook the sock again. He was really getting angry now. I could see some of the veins on his forehead beginning to throb.

"I said, *whose is this?*" Dad demanded. He pointed at Cal. "You. Tell me."

And of course, Cal's instinct was to point to me and shout, "It's Feisal's!"

Dad's favorite thing to do was to ask Kalisha's kids to point the finger whenever there was any wrongdoing. And usually, the finger was pointed away from them and towards us. It never seemed to dawn on Dad that Cal and Maya could lie. Either that or he was just happy to have an excuse to punish my siblings and me.

Dad marched over to me and flicked me in the head as hard as he could. Then, he pointed to the corner of the room and growled through his teeth, "Stand there. *Now.*"

I obeyed, though still sniffling as I tried to insist that the sock wasn't mine. Dad didn't seem to care. He flicked me again and told me to be quiet.

This was only one in a series of events that led me to begin questioning my father's ability to raise kids.

The tragedy of watching this man go from being my best friend in Virginia to a monster that I feared crushed me. I almost didn't recognize him anymore. It was like he'd been body-snatched. He still had the same face, but there was someone new behind his eyes. Someone meaner.

If Mom had been unfit to take care of us kids when she'd suffered her physical decline, why was nobody raising any concerns about Dad's mental sickness? Just because the disease was in his brain didn't make it any less incapacitating.

To be fair, I don't know for sure if Dad ever suffered a diagnosable mental illness. I just know that he was scary and unstable.

Another time something like that happened, it was because of a carton of milk.

Like I said earlier—it sounds ridiculous, doesn't it? But as many writers have said before, sometimes the truth is stranger than fiction.

Dad had opened up the refrigerator looking for something to eat during one of his routine trips to the kitchen when he'd noticed, appallingly, that someone had finished off the milk that he'd bought only two days earlier.

The milk wasn't completely gone. There was still a splash in there—enough to lighten up a cup of coffee or tea. But there wasn't enough to have a satisfying drink.

Dad barged into the family room, where all five of us kids were playing. He held the near-empty milk carton up and demanded to know who'd drank all of it. Of course, none of us answered him. We'd all had some of the milk in our morning cereal. But that wasn't enough to completely drain the carton.

"If nobody comes forward to confess, then all of y'all are getting in trouble," Dad threatened.

Wayne sniffled, beginning to cry. He knew what it meant to get in trouble with Dad.

Cal ran a cost-benefit analysis of throwing me under the bus yet again. And as always, the benefit was far greater to him than the cost was to me. So, he turned to me. In his most innocent voice, he asked, "Feisal, didn't you mention earlier how you had some milk?"

"No," the word shot out of my mouth instantly. I wasn't going to get in trouble again because I wasn't quick enough to defend myself.

"Feisal..." Dad locked his gaze on me. In his eyes, I saw the same terrifying anger that I'd seen on the night that he'd punched me. My heart thrummed in my chest. Was he going to punch me again, right in the middle of the living room in front of all of my siblings?

"Dad, I swear, I didn't-,"

"Lying like a damn child! You need to grow up, Feisal!" Dad snarled. He shook his head as if he were embarrassed of me. "You know what? Get over here."

Dad gestured for me to come to him. I didn't want to move, but my obedient legs carried me over to him regardless. As soon as I was within arms' reach, Dad grabbed me hard by the bicep and yanked me over to him. He practically dragged me down the hall, muttering over and over again, "Get ready for your ass whoopin', boy..."

I didn't know how to respond. Like, how does one prepare for an *ass whoopin'* of all things?

It was beyond me. All I knew was that I was once again in trouble for something that hadn't been my fault in the first place. Dad pulled me into his room, slamming the door behind us. He let me go and told me to sit on his bed. I complied.

Dad squared up with me. Behind him, I could see Kalisha standing in the corner of the room. Her arms were crossed over her chest, and she was leaning on one leg. Her face was stern and smug like an undercover cop catching their perp red-handed.

When Dad looked at me then, his expression was shaded with something. Regret, maybe? Or confliction?

It almost looked like he didn't want to hurt me—but that he didn't have a choice in the matter. It was like someone was forcing him to do this terrible thing. I teared up as I looked at him. I tried to beg him with my eyes to resist whatever cruel force was making him do this.

"Feisal," Dad said. His tone was even but hummed with an undercurrent of rage. "Why did you drink all the damn milk? You know that was supposed to last all of us the whole week. Why'd you do something so selfish like that?"

I shook my head, again telling Dad that it hadn't been me.

Behind him, Kalisha sighed and shook her head. Dad bristled.

"Then who *did?*" he asked me.

My eyes flickered over to Kalisha. She avoided my gaze. It was then that I realized that *she* had been the culprit.

Finally, her eyes met mine. They were burning fiercely, as if to threaten, *"Say it. I dare you."*

I wasn't going to take her bait. I shrugged my shoulders, turning my attention back to Dad. "I don't know who drank it, but it wasn't me. I don't even like milk."

Dad tensed. Kalisha smiled. I realized with a sinking sensation that I had just said something very wrong.

With all the power of an attorney in the middle of a cross-examination, Dad narrowed his eyes and bared his teeth. "You're a damn liar. You have milk with your cereal."

Oh, crap.

He was right, technically. I did have milk with my cereal every morning. But even so, I truly didn't care for milk on its own. When given the option, I preferred to drink juice or even water. When my cereal was finished, I never slurped the rest of the milk from the bowl. I poured it down the sink.

Yet, I'd already made a fatal misstep. And there was no coming back from it. Dad would be sure of that.

One of Kalisha's strict rules in the house was that we kids could not just take food as we pleased. We needed to request permission to eat. This applied to everything: from snacks and treats to full-on meals. The only thing we didn't need to ask for before we helped ourselves to it was water from the tap.

It was then that I realized that the drinking of the milk had not just been one infraction—but two. The first crime was that of not asking permission. The second was that of overindulgence. I was innocent of both charges.

I think deep down, even Dad knew that.

But justice had to be served. And unfortunately, in the process of opening my big, dumb mouth, I'd brought it raining down upon myself.

"Turn around," Dad said.

At first, I didn't know what he was getting at. Part of me was even foolish enough to hope that he was just going to tell me to leave his bedroom and go stand in a corner or something. Instead, as I pivoted on my heels, I heard something metallic unbuckling. His belt.

I barely had time to brace myself.

The leather hitting my butt was nothing like I had ever experienced before. It was sharp and biting and so damn painful.

Dad didn't stop at one lash, though. He kept going. He beat me mercilessly, the sound of the leather thwapping against my backside loud enough to ring in my ears. If this wasn't enough punishment, I was also humiliated by the fact that Kalisha was there to witness it all. I stared at her, helpless. I quietly begged her to make Dad stop. To tell him the truth. That *she* had been the one to drink the milk. He certainly wouldn't beat her with a belt. He'd probably just get huffy.

But Kalisha didn't say anything. In fact, she almost looked *happy.* Like she was enjoying my suffering.

Eventually, I began counting the hits. It distracted me just enough to keep me sane.

I lost count twice.

It was like once Dad had gotten himself going, he didn't know how to stop. I don't even think that he was fully conscious of what he was doing.

Eventually, the pain became too much to bear. I collapsed forward on the floor. I was crying my eyes out, and begging Dad to stop. Blessedly, he snapped out of whatever hypnotic stupor he was in. He stepped back, coolly fixing his belt back around his hips as if nothing had happened at all.

For days, I was not able to sit down comfortably. At school, I felt humiliated every time I had to awkwardly sit down at a desk, wincing as the hard plastic pressed up against my bruises. I practically limped around campus.

At home, it was even worse. After eight hours of gritting my teeth through the pain, all I wanted to do was lay down in my bed. But under Kalisha's rule, I was not allowed to. Kalisha didn't like us being too comfortable in our house. She either wanted us sitting on the floor or at the table quietly doing homework or reading.

Unlike the night that Dad punched me, I did not wonder if the beating over the milk actually happened. I did not mistake it for a bad dream. How could I, when I was reminded of its reality every time I so much as sat down?

This time, when I saw Dad at the kitchen table, I did not expect or even hope to receive an apology. Which I guess was a good thing—because it was clear that Dad did not intend to give me one.

Chapter 18

SHHH...PRIVATE THOUGHTS

"**W**hat the hell are you two whispering about in there?" Kalisha burst through the door into the bedroom that I shared with Wayne and Cal. Her eyes were narrowed with suspicion. "You know you ain't supposed to talk about *that place.*"

The way she said it, you would've thought *that place* referred to Hell.

Except for Kalisha, *that place* meant Virginia.

"No, ma'am," Wayne said, his voice soft. He blinked up at her with his big brown eyes. "We were just talking about some of Feisal's friends at school."

Kalisha clicked her tongue. She wasn't buying Wayne's lie, but apparently, she also didn't think it was worth fussing over any further.

With a scoff, she turned around. "Better not have been." She stormed out of the room, keeping the door wide open as a warning to Wayne and me that a private conversation was a luxury that we could not afford.

Kalisha always got petty like this whenever anyone talked about Virginia. She didn't like being reminded that Dad had lived a life before her. She didn't like that Dad had been in love with another woman before her. God only knows why she was so jealous. It wasn't like Mom was going to come back from the dead to steal Dad away from her.

The funny thing is, even if Mom *did* come back from the dead, it's not like she would've wanted Dad anyway.

Because of Kalisha's hatred of Virginia and all that the state represented, Wayne, Rhondelle, and I often convened to reminisce in secret. We talked about how we missed our old life. How we missed our old school and our friends. How we missed Grandma, and Aunt Nina, and Mom.

But every time we dared to talk about our old life, it seemed that someone was waiting around the corner, listening. If not Kalisha, then Cal.

We could never catch a break under Kalisha's roof. Not even our memories were safe from her iron fist. All we had were our private thoughts. And sometimes even those, it seemed, were off-limits.

Chapter 19

NINETY-DEGREE ANGLE

Our punishments from Dad did not stop and end at his fist. Sometimes they involved a different kind of physicality.

The first time Dad made Wayne, Rhondelle, and me squat with books was because we had gotten into a fight with Kalisha's kids. When Rhondelle mouthed off to Dad, asking him why he wasn't punishing *them,* Dad just muttered something like, *"You mind your own business. They'll get taken care of."*

Taken care of, my ass. I had to stop myself from groaning.

In order to punish all three of us at once, Dad went into our bookbags and grabbed all of our heavy hardback textbooks. He put two books in each of our hands. I got the heaviest two. Wayne and Rhondelle got slightly lighter loads.

Then, Dad told us to go stand along the wall (but not against it). From there, he instructed us to hold our books out in front of us and to squat down. We had to squat with proper form, meaning that our knees were bent almost at a ninety-degree angle.

It only took minutes for my entire body to start burning. My thighs and calves ached from the squat, and my arms ached from the books. My younger siblings weren't faring any better than I was. Wayne whimpered, dropping his arms so that his elbows could rest against his thighs.

Dad had none of this shortcutting. He snapped his fingers in front of Wayne's face, warning him that if he didn't squat right, he'd have to suffer the punishment for even longer. Wayne grimaced, returning his arms to their previous position.

After ten minutes of this punishment, I was practically dying. Every particle in my body begged to relax. My hands sweated, and my nose felt itchy. My legs trembled.

Finally, Dad let us off the hook.

He warned us that this would be his new way of teaching us lessons.

At first, I thought that this wasn't so bad. Especially as I rubbed the soreness out of my arms and legs. Sure, it wasn't exactly *fun*. But it beat being hit over and over again with a belt.

As always, I quickly learned to watch what I wished for.

A mere ten-minute squat must have not been enough suffering for Dad's liking. Because he quickly upped the time to one hour. Then two hours. Until suddenly, we were just told to squat until he allowed us to stop.

We would only be allowed to go to the bathroom before we began our punishment. If you were an hour into a squat with two hours left to go and you had to pee, you were out of luck. If we got in trouble during the week, we'd be given some break time to do our homework. As soon as we were done, we had to go right back to squatting with the books.

The best part about the punishment (at least as far as Dad was concerned) was that he could carry it out even when he was on the road. Once he told Kalisha about his ingenious new form of corporal punishment, it was all over for us. She had us squatting for just about everything. For talking back. For forgetting an assignment. Even, it seemed, for *breathing* too loud.

Withstanding the pain of a squat for a few minutes was tough. Withstanding it for hours was sheer torture. I'd be squatting for so long that my entire body would hurt days afterward. My sore muscles would scream in protest whenever I so much as lifted myself up from a chair or brought my fork to my mouth during dinner.

During the squat, my feet would sweat and affect my balance. My fatigued grip would loosen around the books that I was holding.

But I didn't dare fall. Nor did I dare rest. When we squatted, we were forced to stand within the eyeline of a witness. If we so much as wobbled, it had to be reported to Kalisha. And then, Kalisha would tell us that our egregious loss of balance had earned us another five minutes of the squat.

When neither Kalisha nor Dad was home, Cal watched us. And he took his job as seriously as a prison warden.

If it wasn't embarrassing enough that I was being supervised by someone younger than myself, we also had to ask Cal if we could go to the bathroom whenever nature struck. And Cal would sigh and wave us off, as though he was doing some great favor by allowing us to use the restroom in our own house.

All of us took our sweet time in the bathroom whenever we were given permission to use it. Every second spent in the bathroom was a second that we didn't have to be squatting.

But the sanctuary was always fleeting. Our house had seven occupants and one bathroom, after all. Nobody ever had the chance to hog it.

Sometimes Cal would even knock on the bathroom himself, knowing what we were up to. It was almost as if he *enjoyed* watching us struggle as we squatted with the books.

There would be times when I'd ask Cal to use the bathroom, and instead of saying yes or no, he'd just shrug and reply, "What the hell are you asking me for?"

Anytime he said that I knew that what he really wanted to say was, "No." But even kids like Cal tended to have hearts—and he knew that denying us the restroom was inhumane. Still, he kept tabs. He'd count the number of times we went to the bathroom. And he kept a mental ledger of how many seconds or minutes we'd spent in there.

Then, once Kalisha or Dad got back, he'd report his findings to them dutifully.

"Also, Feisal went to the bathroom without getting my permission," he'd add, purposefully omitting the fact that I *had* asked permission and that *he* had given me a crappy, noncommittal answer.

Looking back, I don't even blame Cal for being such a little jerk. Sure, what he was doing was immature and cruel. But he wasn't the only one responsible for his behavior. It was the adults—Kalisha and Dad—who validated his behavior by always taking his word and giving him the reactions he desired.

While the amount of time that we were forced to hold the books for each punishment varied, the lengths of our sentences were generally based on whatever Kalisha thought we deserved. Sometimes, if the infraction was slight, we'd only have to squat for a few minutes. But if something we did really angered her, we'd be forced to sit with the books until she was satisfied. And that could take *days*.

Literally.

There were several times in which I'd done something (or, more accurately, Cal had *said* that I'd done something) that had earned me a forty-eight-hour punishment. In those

142

cases, I was given a strict eating and sleeping schedule to adhere to. Every second not on that schedule was reserved for the punishment.

Nighttime always felt like a blessing during these long stretches. During the night, everyone would retreat to the bedrooms, meaning that nobody was surveilling me. That gave me the freedom to stand up straight.

I'd stand upright, the books hanging loosely at my hips, until I heard movement. Then, I'd quickly fall back into my squat position, pretending as though I'd been holding it firmly the entire time.

During these parts of the punishment, I often fantasized about sleep. I dreamed of how good it would feel to be in my bed, my weary body finally permitted to rest.

Sometimes Dad and Kalisha would forget to send me to bed at all and I'd spend the entire night awake, squatting. The next morning, Dad would shuffle into the living room and see me there—still holding the books—and he'd frown.

"Boy, is your ass *still* standing there?" He'd ask—as if this was something that *I'd* chosen to do.

Jesus, I'd think, baffled, *did this man honestly forget about my ass standing here all night?*

I wouldn't say that part out loud, though.

Instead, I'd just nod and try to look as pitiful as possible so that he'd let me off the hook. This wasn't hard since these all-nighters had me feeling half-dead anyway.

Out of the three of us, Wayne and I were the ones forced into this punishment the most. Rhondelle still got her fair share, though. I have this distinct memory of carrying out the punishment with Wayne and looking at him, feeling so bad for the little body that was expected to hold the books as steadfastly as mine did.

I know every kid likes to insist that they "didn't do anything." Especially when punishments are involved. But for Wayne, Rhondelle, and I—it was true. We really didn't do anything. The only thing that we had ever done was *exist*.

Apparently in Kalisha's court of law, daring to exist was the greatest crime of all.

Anything that went wrong in the house was at the fault of my siblings and me—even if there was no evidence to prove that we'd committed any wrongdoing. It wasn't fair. But what could we do?

Even Wayne, as loving and as trusting as he was, couldn't understand why we were being treated like this.

Sometimes, we would stand for so long that we couldn't help but reposition ourselves. The strategy Wayne and I both employed involved shifting all our weight to one leg. When that leg couldn't endure another second, we'd switch to the other.

This only worked if there were no adults in the nearby vicinity. If Dad caught us doing that, he'd demand for us to straighten ourselves. When we were being punished, he watched our every move.

The pain of squatting for hours on end with the books was bad enough. The mental drudgery was what really killed me. Plain and simple: it was *boring*. We obviously weren't allowed to go anywhere or do anything. We weren't even allowed to talk other than to ask for the bathroom. To pass the time and to distract myself from the pain, I'd play little games in my head.

I'd time how long it took for people to finish different topics in their conversations. I'd sing songs in my head but rearrange the lyrics to fit my life. P!nk's Sober could be sung on its own: *When it's good/Then it's good, it's so good till it goes bad.* Yep. No edits needed there.

After a while, I gave up on the ultimate existential question: *"why me?"*

I realized that it wouldn't matter even if I had the answer. The answer wouldn't speed up the passage of time while I was being forced to squat. The answer wouldn't ease the pain of my legs or the exhaustion of my body.

I gave up on trying to understand why Dad thought this was an acceptable form of punishment. I gave up wondering what we ever did to deserve it.

Instead of these abstract concepts, I focused on what I concretely knew.

And what I concretely knew was exactly where my siblings and I stood with my father. It was clear as day. Dad had built his second family already. He'd run away for a reason. And then, like a zit, Wayne, Rhondelle, and I had resurfaced. We got in the way. We ruined things.

I felt like Dad hated me. And those feelings weren't exactly unfounded.

We didn't connect anymore. I didn't recognize his eyes or his smile. Sometimes, discreetly, I stared at him—trying to peel back the exterior layers in hopes that I'd find a glimmer of something that reminded me of the man that he used to be. The man that I'd idolized. But every time, I came up short.

Sometimes, I'd drop the books. It wouldn't be on purpose. I wasn't trying to be petulant. I was often just tired and lost my grip.

But whenever that happened, Dad took it as a personal afront. He'd glare at me. Then, without saying anything, he'd storm away to his bedroom. He'd grab his favorite belt (yes, he had a *favorite* belt to beat his kids with), and he'd hit me as hard as he could. He'd hit me continuously until I got back into my squatting position.

He wouldn't even give me a moment to readjust.

When you're being hit by a grown man, there's simply no way *not* to drop your books a second time. I learned quickly that if I wanted him to stop swinging that belt, I had to be able to endure at least one hit while maintaining my proper squatting position.

I remember praying, *"Please. Please help me hold these books. Please don't let them fall. Please."*

Sometimes if people came to the house, Dad would release us from our punishment until they were gone. It was a sign that deep down, even he knew that what he was doing was wrong. Occasionally, even after they left, Dad would forget all about our punishment. Of course, in those cases, Cal usually took it upon himself to remind Dad that we'd not yet served our full sentence.

During one of my squatting sessions, the doorbell rang.

Excitement and relief filled my chest. *A break!*

Usually, when the doorbell rang, it meant that Kalisha's dad or stepmom had come for a visit. Her dad was a painter and handyman. He was over whenever there was an issue in the house if Dad wasn't around to fix it. I wasn't close with him—he rarely even looked at any of us kids—but I didn't mind him. Kalisha seemed to have a similar opinion about her dad. One of quiet ambivalence.

Her stepmom, however, was the complete opposite.

Whenever Kalisha's stepmom, Jada, came over, Kalisha *laughed.* She laughed a lot. And she smiled, too.

I almost never saw Kalisha smiling or laughing—so the first time I heard her belly-laugh around Jada, I was shocked.

Jada always came well-dressed. She exclusively wore in-season dresses or skirts and blouses straight off the department store racks. She was not the type of woman to believe in *clearance deals.* She had a pair of high-heels in every color, and I always knew when she came to visit because I'd be able to hear the *click-click-click* of them through the windows as she trotted up our driveway to the front door. Her bags were Chanel, and large enough to conceal a small dog.

She was good-looking for her age. Her teeth were so perfect that she could've been scouted for a Colgate advertisement.

I couldn't imagine how her relationship with Kalisha's dad worked. He always seemed so simple and modest.

Maybe opposites really *did* attract.

Jada didn't come over too often. But as I heard the unmistakable *click-click-click* of heels against our entryway tile, I knew that it was her.

I waited patiently for Kalisha to come over to me and tell me that my punishment was on pause. Or at the very least for me to move to a different part of the house so that I wouldn't be seen by Jada.

But she didn't.

As Jada entered the house, I stayed where I was. Humiliation scorched my body as Jada walked into the living room and saw me squatting there with my books. A modern-day equivalent of a town fool in the pillory.

Jada walked up to me, all smiles.

"How are you doing, Feisal?" she asked, her voice honeyed.

How does it look like I'm doing?

I forced myself to refrain from grimacing. It didn't seem like Jada was trying to be rude. In fact, she seemed like she was being *nice* to me. So, I did my best to nod politely and smile back—though I probably looked more like a dog baring its teeth.

Over the next few minutes, Jada and Kalisha settled into the room. They talked about inconsequential things, unbothered by my presence. At first, I thought that Jada was just tolerating me there. But then, they started talking *about* me, and my whole perspective on the situation changed.

"He's a problem," Kalisha bemoaned, casting a look in my direction. "He's like a ringleader in this house. He does something bad, and the rest of them follow after him like they've lost their ability to think for themselves. I wonder if he's threatening them."

Threatening? I couldn't believe what I was hearing. I wanted to speak up, but I knew that doing so would invoke even further punishment. So, I let her blaspheme.

"You better to send him to *kiddie jail,*" Jada said, raising her eyebrows. "You know, that's where they sent that little Chris boy when you were in junior high. I remember talking to his mom about it, and she said..."

Jada didn't have to use a code word. I knew what she was referring to when she said *kiddie jail*. She was talking about the youth behavioral facilities that Dad had already threatened to send me to if I "kept stepping out of line."

Kalisha played dumb. "Oh, what's that? Is it safe? We don't want to put Feisal in any danger."

My jaw clenched. She was flat-out lying! And she wasn't even doing a particularly good job of it. Why not just tell Jada that she and Dad had already threatened me numerous times with a stay at the facility? What was the point of the theatrics?

As Kalisha listened emphatically to her stepmother talk about the boons of *scaring me straight* with one of those facilities, I began to fume. Especially when Kalisha confessed her reasons for considering the facility at all.

"He's just an angry kid. He won't listen. Not to me or his daddy."

"All the more reason. If he doesn't listen to you two, he might listen to one of the officers that work there. They're all business. Plus, it might discourage him from disobeying in the future. You know, I saw this segment on the news that mentioned that kids who disobey their parents end up more likely to go to jail."

I was so frustrated, tears pricked at my eyes.

"We'll think about it," Kalisha said.

Then, she stood up and excused herself to the restroom. As soon as she left the room, Jada turned to look at me.

At first, I thought she was looking at something else. Maybe there was a new decoration up on the wall above my head that I'd somehow neglected to notice. She'd spent the entire conversation talking about me as if I wasn't in the room—and now it seemed as if she'd just taken stock of my existence again. It was as if she'd suffered a temporary bout of blindness during her conversation with Kalisha.

She looked around, almost timidly, then approached me. In a hushed voice, she said, "You want to leave?"

At first, I didn't respond. I was too stunned to say a word.

"You want to leave?" she asked again. "Do you want me to sneak you into my car?"

I blinked. *Is this woman for real?*

I didn't know what to do. Didn't know what to say. Jada's words now were so at odds with what she had just been telling Kalisha.

Could it all have been a front? She looked so sincere now. Maybe she was honestly trying to bust me out and had just said all that stuff to get Kalisha's guard down.

"Come on, Feisal. Before your mom gets back." She sounded almost urgent.

What if this is my shot?

I knew already that I wouldn't get a chance like this again. I could already taste the air outside the house. Could already feel the rumble of Jada's sedan beneath my legs as we peeled out of the driveway and down the street toward freedom.

Nodding, I started to lower my books.

But I was too late.

I heard the bathroom door open, and Kalisha walking down the hall. Instinctively, my arms went rigid again, holding out the books as though my resolve had never wavered at all.

Damn. I was too slow.

Jada straightened as Kalisha entered the room. Her gentle face took on a new air of disgust as she regarded me—again staring down at me as if I were lower than the dirt beneath her designer heels.

"You won't believe this, Kalisha," Jada said, crossing her arms. "As soon as you walked out of the room, he asked me to take him out of here in my car."

Instantly, my heart plummeted. It had all been a trap. Jada hadn't been trying to help me. She'd been testing me all along.

I was such an idiot. Why had I trusted this woman? How had I watched her laugh with Kalisha countless times—only to earnestly believe that she would turn against her?

Hope had clouded my judgment. And now, as I squatted there, I was forced to wallow in my shame and humiliation as Jada and Kalisha went on even more feverishly about my poor behavior and my future destiny as a prison inmate.

"I should've taken him," Jada said, shaking her head in an *oh, kids these days* kind of fashion. "I would've dropped him off on the freeway. Would've let someone snatch his ass right up."

Please, God. If only, I thought bitterly.

Between being kidnapped and hurt by a stranger or being stuck in my own hellish house—I would've taken the stranger any day.

Kalisha and Jada looked at me, laughing. Like how kids laugh at ants being burned on the sidewalk by a magnifying glass. It was the most degrading experience of my life to date.

It was hours before Jada finally left. When she did, I heard her tell Kalisha, "I have thicker books at my house. I'll bring them next time for him to hold."

Chapter 20

DEFENDING DAD-FISTICUFFS

There's this common saying that I hated as a kid— that things get *better.* Maybe I hated it so much because, for me, things only ever seemed to get worse.

If it was any consolation, things seemed to be going poorly for the whole *family,* and not just me. A few months after the move, Dad and Kalisha began arguing. Dad and Mom's arguments had always been a little hushed. Almost out of decency. Even when Mom had found out about Dad's cheating, the only reason I'd been able to hear her was because I'd actively been eavesdropping.

Dad's arguments with Kalisha were not quite so discreet.

The two of them would argue all night. They'd call each other every unholy name in the book. Then, one of them would get a little too pissed off and leave the house. They'd speed off in the car, and we wouldn't see them again for a while. A few hours if it was Kalisha. A few days if it was my dad.

I could always tell who'd left. The parent that remained would tromp about the house like a belligerent toddler, still yelling and making comments toward the other.

Me and my siblings learned quickly to deal with it.

Better them be angry at each other than at us, I thought.

Unfortunately, their anger with one another didn't *distract* from their anger with us. Rather, it *fueled* it.

Dad's method of serving justice in our house had always been cruel. But now, when he hit me or Wayne—it wasn't just out of irritation or a misplaced sense of parental responsibility. It was out of anger.

The only way I can even start to rationalize it is that Dad was going through a lot of pain. And maybe he thought that he could transfer that pain to us. Over time, his punches became less forgiving. His sneers were colder. Even his eyes were harsher.

And yet, I still wanted to defend him.

I glared at Cal from across the room, my eyes narrowed into slits.

Dad had gotten into an argument with Kalisha recently. In her typical fashion, Kalisha was telling her kids all kinds of garbage about what had caused the fight. This was Kalisha's typical strategy. She knew that she couldn't stand up to Dad on her own. But if she could manipulate her kids into standing with her, she could buy herself a little bit more leverage.

Now, hours later, Cal was running his mouth about all the stuff Kalisha had said.

"Your daddy's no good," Cal asserted, shaking his head like he had the audacity to be *sorry* for me. "He's a bum."

"We wouldn't even be *in* this house without my dad," I shot back. "It's not like *Kalisha's* lazy butt works."

"Yeah, she does. She takes care of us, dummy," Cal shot back. "Besides, none of this would be happening if you guys weren't here. We can't afford anything nice anymore because of you. Because your daddy has three extra mouths to feed." Cal was probably plagiarizing his mother word-for-word. He probably didn't even know what he was saying. But it riled me up anyways.

"How is that our fault?" I asked.

"Because you called him," Cal replied as if it was the simplest conclusion to draw in the world. "Your daddy didn't even want you guys here. He's just keeping you in his house because that's what he's supposed to do."

"Not true."

Cal could tell that he was getting a rise out of me, and he was delighting in it. I so badly wanted to smack that stupid self-righteous grin off his face. Even though my relationship with Dad was almost nonexistent at that point, I refused to let anyone speak poorly of him. Least of all Cal.

"Yeah-huh. Face it, Feisal. Your daddy is a *B-U-M.*"

I'd had enough.

I got to my feet and tackled Cal. Cal yelped as I knocked him to the floor. It took him a few seconds to react.

When he finally got his wits about him, he began to wrestle back.

We were a flurry of adolescent rage. Arms swinging, feet kicking, hands grabbing. We were like wild animals—biting and snapping and scratching at every patch of exposed skin.

Rhondelle and Maya tried to break us up, but by the time they'd gotten to us, we were completely consumed by our fight. Unable to cease the wrestling, Wayne jumped in to assist me. Maybe he thought that if we could knock out Cal together, everything would be over faster.

Eventually, Cal realized that he was sorely outnumbered and outmatched. He crumpled to the floor and wriggled away from Wayne and me. He was sniveling. Crying about how unfair the fight had been.

"You wouldn't be acting so tough if you didn't have your stupid little brother helping you," Cal said, disregarding the fact that I'd been beating him even before Wayne had jumped in to help.

With his tail between his legs, Cal slinked away.

At first, I was almost hopeful that the humiliation of losing would keep Cal from talking about the fight. I should have known better. Cal had a greater vested interest in punishing me than he did in preserving himself.

When Dad came back home two days later to make up with Kalisha, I learned this truth the hard way.

Dad called Wayne into his room first. He said that he just wanted to *talk,* but we all knew by now that "talk" was just a code word for an ass-whooping. I felt my heart sink into my chest as I watched Wayne march back there. It was like watching your best mate on a pirate ship being forced to walk the plank.

I already knew what Wayne was getting in trouble for.

And I knew that if *he* was getting in trouble for it—it was only a matter of time before my own judgment day arrived.

I cringed as I heard the noises coming from Dad's room. A beating. The door being closed muffled some of the sounds, but just enough of it crept out to make my blood run cold. When Wayne came back into our bedroom from Dad's, his fists were balled and his eyes were bloodshot. He was fighting back tears.

It killed me to see him like that.

Wayne had always been a ray of sunshine. This sadness was foreign on his face.

"Dad wants to see you," he mumbled out, eyes momentarily flickering to me.

I nodded. A pit had already formed in my stomach. My only saving grace was my honest defense—that I had only wrestled with Cal in order to protect my father's honor. I forced a stoic expression, not wanting to show Wayne how truly terrified I was.

Then, I got up and walked to Dad's room.

He was waiting for me when I walked in. Kalisha was right there next to him. Her arms were crossed stiffly over her chest. I took my sweet time closing the door behind me. The latch clicking into place sounded like a gun cocking.

Dad glared at me. He wasn't sweating or panting. He'd gone easy on Wayne. It was a small consolation that was quickly extinguished by the realization that he was probably saving his hardest hits for *me*.

"Feisal. Why'd you and Wayne try to jump Cal?"

I blinked. Was *that* the story that Cal had told Kalisha?

"I didn't. We didn't," I asserted.

Dad didn't wait for me to state the rest of my case. He lurched forward, his fist nailing my chest in one swift blow. I staggered back, tears pricking my eyes. It took me a second to catch my breath again.

"We didn't!" I said again, this time with a little more conviction. I held my hand up, begging for an inch of grace. I needed to say my peace. I needed to convince Dad that I had fought for *him*. It was my only chance of escaping his room unscathed. "Cal was talking trash about you, Dad."

159

"Oh, was he?" Kalisha's voice was pitchy. She was on the defensive. Probably because she knew that anything that left her son's mouth only served to reflect her own thoughts. "What did he say, then?"

I didn't look at Kalisha. I kept my eyes trained on Dad. "He called you a bum. He said you were no good."

"Stop lying," Kalisha hissed.

I balked. "I'm not! I told him to stop bad-mouthing you, Dad, but he wouldn't. So, I had to make him stop. I was only trying to defend you."

"You keep lying on my son, and you're going to have to deal with me," Kalisha threatened.

I rolled my eyes at her. "Whatever."

In an instant, I realized that I'd made a fatal mistake. "Whatever" was, in fact, exactly what I *shouldn't* have said.

If I'd won any points with Dad previously, they'd all been dashed now. He looked at me like I was the scum of the earth. A cancer that had to be eradicated for the good of the organism.

He punched me again, so hard that he literally knocked me off my feet. I collapsed to the ground, clutching my chest. It hurt so bad that I started to cry.

Over the sound of my sobs and the blood rushing in my ears, I heard Kalisha snap, "Get your ass up!"

160

So used to doing exactly as I was told, I staggered to my feet.

What I didn't expect was for *Kalisha* to take a shot at me. She punched me, too. In the exact same place that Dad had hit me twice already. She couldn't hit as hard as Dad— not by a long shot—but the shock of being hit by her caught me unprepared. I gasped, hands flying up to my chest to protect it from any further damage.

"You kidding me right now?" Dad taunted. "You're this worked up over a woman hitting you? Man up, Feisal. Come on."

I couldn't even look at him. It apparently meant nothing to him that I was still a child and Kalisha was a full-grown woman.

"Fight me, boy," Dad commanded. I shook my head, *no.* Dad scoffed. "Why the hell not? You worried that I'm bigger than you? That I'll hurt you? That *she'll* hurt you? Yeah, it's not fun when two people gang up on you, is it?"

I knew that he was trying to make a point to me about how it hadn't been fair for Wayne and me to wrestle Cal two-on-one. But this didn't seem equivalent to what we had done.

"Cal!" Dad shouted. "Get in here!"

Cal was in the room within seconds. Before I knew what was happening, Dad grabbed me by the back of my shirt collar and yanked me back to him. He pinned my arms at my sides with his large hands. Then he told Cal to hit me. To "teach me a lesson" about starting fights that I couldn't finish.

"Hit him," he encouraged. "Don't hold back."

Cal was perfectly happy to oblige. He punched my stomach and chest multiple times, as hard as he could. I tried to block his hits with my arms, but Dad kept them pinned to my side and kept snarling, *"Quit it, Feisal. You're learning a lesson."* over and over in my ear.

The worst part of it all was that Cal didn't know the first thing about throwing a *real* punch. His blows weren't fast and discreet like Dad's were. When he punched, he imitated his beloved anime programs. Every time he took a swing, he'd shake his head—almost as if he imagined the camera taking a dramatic angle on his face to catch his reaction. He punched me with one hand, leaving the other straight. And when he wound up for harder hits, he growled, *"Kamehameha!"* under his breath like Goku did in *Dragon Ball Z.*

If I was in any less of a sorry state, I probably would've laughed at him. It was all so ridiculous.

After Cal got his fill of beating me up, Dad let me go. I stalked back to my room and crumpled into a heap on my bed. My body ached all over. Even then, I could tell that the dull pain was going to stick with me for a while.

The next morning, I checked myself in the mirror to inspect the damage that had been done. There was one dark purple spot—where Dad and Kalisha had both punched me—and a flurry of other, lighter marks. If my skin were any paler, the bruising from Cal's punches would've been clearly visible. But in the dim bathroom, they blended into the rest of my flesh.

As I looked at my hurt body, I thought of Mom. I thought of how fiercely she'd been against Dad putting his hands on us. I wondered if she was still proud of me. If somehow, my blemishes were a sign that I'd failed her.

I worried that she wouldn't be able to relax in heaven, knowing what her babies were being put through.

I'm sorry, Mom, I thought. *If I knew how to save us, I would.*

Chapter 21

JOINING FORCES &
OUTNUMBERED

*I*n a different life, I might've gotten along with Cal. Hell, maybe we could've been friends. In our house on Chester Street, though, we had no chance.

Cal and I had started out on rough terms. We'd both battled for dominance under the same roof—not quite realizing that we both lost whenever Dad entered the equation. Yet, over time, our relationship started to relax a little.

Slowly, we all started to assimilate into a family unit. We all began to see one another as siblings. In my head, Cal and Maya became my brother and sister in the same way that Wayne and Rhondelle were. Of course, there was always a little bit of extra distance between us as we had come from different places. But regardless of where we'd started—we were all *here* now.

And sticking together was a hell of a lot more pleasant than constantly being at one another's throats.

The problem, as always, seemed to arise when Dad and Kalisha entered the mix.

Even though Cal and Maya were starting to accept us as their siblings, Kalisha was less thrilled about the idea of us mixing in with each other. She didn't like the fact that we were getting along. She didn't like that Maya was starting to spend more time with Rhondelle than with her birth-brother.

That's when she started intervening.

It was little things at first. Kalisha would say little things to insinuate that things between us were not quite as smooth as they seemed. *"Cal, weren't you just telling me how you hate that Feisal never cleans up his side of the room?"* and, *"I think Wayne's giving you a dirty look, Maya,"* and *"You three don't have to pretend to get along, you know. I have eyes."*

The thing about Kalisha was that she always knew exactly what to say to open old wounds. And she always knew *when* to say it to maximize our reactions. She could reignite fights from hours, days, even weeks ago with a single sly comment.

With her in our ears, things never stayed peaceful amongst us kids for long. Even at our best moments, Kalisha could tear us down and get us at each other's throats again. She seemed to enjoy doing it, too. She was like one of those crooked reality TV show producers, stirring up drama for her own entertainment.

One day, Cal got into a fight at school. I don't know exactly what happened. If I had to guess, I'd say that Cal had probably mouthed off to the wrong person. All I knew was that one moment, I was talking with my friends in the courtyard—and the next, Maya was dragging me off in a desperate attempt to call in some backup for her brother who was getting pummeled by the basketball hoops.

I didn't even think before jumping in to help him.

The fight didn't last much longer after my intervention. The other kids had started to get tired, and I was fresh into the fray. It was easy for me to push them off Cal. Cal thanked me after the fight, clapping me on the shoulder. It didn't matter that we were at each other's throats constantly at home. When it came down to it, we could be depended on to protect one another. It was one of the few moments of brotherhood that I think we genuinely shared.

Which meant that naturally, Kalisha had to ruin it.

When we got home that evening, Kalisha noticed a bruise on Cal's chin. When she asked how it had gotten there, Maya confessed that Cal had gotten into a fight—and that I had helped him fend off the attackers. Cal emphatically confirmed Maya's story.

"He had my back, Mom. He really did," Cal said.

Kalisha crinkled up her nose. She looked between Cal and me. I think Kalisha realized early on that with Dad constantly out of the house—we kids outnumbered her five-to-one. If all of us joined forces against her, her leverage and power would dissolve like a tissue in hot water. So, the only way for her to survive was to continually drive wedges between us that fractured our power.

And right now, as Cal continued to talk about how we'd teamed up against his attackers, and about how grateful he was that he could rely on me, it dawned on her that her two strongest links were starting to connect into a single chain.

She brought out the cutters swiftly and without mercy.

"I don't know, baby. Those kids are probably going to think that you're a punk now," she hummed.

"What do you mean?" Cal's brow furrowed.

"They're going to think that you can't hold your own. That you need Feisal to help you stand up for yourself. Honestly, things might turn out worse. Hell, I might even have to call the school."

Cal seemed to register what his mother was saying. He looked at me as if suddenly seeing me in a different light. Gone was the gratitude and friendliness in his eyes that had graced me earlier. In its place was a new shimmer of distrust.

"Anyways, I've seen how boys your age fight. Arms swinging everywhere—not even sure what you are and aren't hitting. I'll bet that mark on your chin wasn't even from one of those bullies. Actually, Feisal, can I see your elbow?"

Without waiting for my reply, she grabbed my elbow and brought it up, gently tapping it against Cal's bruise—as if that was supposed to prove anything. Regardless, she nodded, as if she'd just given perfect evidence to show that I'd committed an unforgivable act of friendly fire.

"Well, he *was* trying to help," Cal muttered, though he seemed more unsure of himself now.

"Good intentions or not. I don't think he really did you any favors," Kalisha said. "He should've just stayed out of it."

Except I *couldn't* have stayed out of it. Even though Cal made my life a living hell on a regular basis, it wasn't in me to stand by while he got beat up. Plus, if I had let him lose the fight, I would've had to hear it at home for *not* stepping in.

Little did I know, I'd be hearing it at home either way.

At that point, Cal was totally convinced that my act of goodwill was actually an evil deed in disguise. And I was so over everything at that point that I didn't even have it in me to defend myself to him later when we were alone in our room.

I was tired of not being able to do anything right. I was tired of always being painted out to be the villain. It felt like no matter how I acted, I was always going to be the asshole in everyone's eyes. And there was nothing I could do about it.

Damned if you do, and damned if you don't. God, if only there were some magical third option. I would've taken it in a heartbeat.

Every now and again, Cal would say something that made me wonder if he actually *did* care after all. We'd be sitting alone in our room. I'd be nursing some bruise or ache that Dad had given me earlier that day. And Cal would just open his mouth and say it, "Sorry, Feisal."

I'd turn my head at him, confused for a moment.

"I'm sorry that you're always being treated this way." He'd fidget with his hands as he spoke. He'd avert his eyes. As if he knew, even subconsciously, the fragment of guilt he bore. "It's just because you're the oldest, you know? That's why you always have to take the blame for everything."

I scoffed.

"Look," Cal added, a little colder than before. "I don't think it's fair. I think you're being cheated."

It dawned on me that Cal might be right. Being the oldest boy in the house meant that Dad had the least reservations about putting his hands on me. He'd never smack around Rhondelle like he did me. And even when he hit Wayne, it wasn't usually as bad as the beatings that I was starting to get used to.

I wasn't sure how to feel about Cal apologizing back then. I'm still not entirely sure how I feel about it now. Now detached from my childhood by age and wisdom, I can freely retrospect on the situation. I can see that it wasn't fair for any of us to be in that house. Even though I was getting the worst of it, my siblings—Cal and Maya included—got it bad, too.

Is the bitterness that I still sometimes feel valid? Or was that, too, one of Kalisha's inventions?

I don't know. I probably never will.

I'm learning to make my peace with that fact.

Cal and I weren't the only two that Kalisha wanted to drive a wedge between. She also hated the bond that I shared with Wayne.

She did everything she could to pit us against each other. She'd verbally manipulate us. She'd get us in trouble, and then offer us an out *if and only if* we threw the other under the bus. And when none of that soft psychology worked, Kalisha brought out the big guns: Dad.

Dad took a much more direct route of forcing us to hurt one another. He'd wait until we got in trouble. Then, he'd lock us in a room together. He'd tell us that he was going to let us "work out our punishment amongst one another."

Then, he'd force us to fight.

It only happened a few times. But each brawl that I was forced to endure with my brother was pure Hell.

I tried to hold my punches back. I tried to aim for the strong muscle of his chest and arms, rather than the softer, more vulnerable tissue at his stomach. Wayne exercised the same restraint towards me.

But Dad was no dummy. He caught on to us quickly and warned us that if we didn't start hitting one another like we meant it, he'd intervene. And since both Wayne and I knew that Dad's weakest punches could dwarf our strongest ones, we began hitting more fiercely.

I saw those strikes against my brother as a mercy. My fist in place of Dad's. And still, causing my little brother any pain tore me apart.

Afterward, we'd lick our wounds. We'd pretend all afternoon that Kalisha and Dad had thoroughly sparked some bad blood between us. And then, later that night, we'd meet up to forgive one another.

Kalisha's mind games may have worked between Cal and me. But she was never going to get Wayne and me to hate each other. We just had too much history. Too much love.

And deep down, I think we both knew that if we started hating each other, Mom's soul would never rest easy.

When Dad dragged me out of my room, my first thought was, *what did I do this time?*

It was automatic now for me to assume responsibility for every little thing that went wrong in the house. From dirty dishes to an unexpectedly high gas bill. Somehow, Dad could always trace the crime back to me.

As Dad pulled me, still half-asleep, into the hallway, I wondered irritably what I was being charged with this time.

Was I snoring too loud? Dreaming too disruptively? Laying in an improper manner?

Dad brought me into his bedroom. His eyes looked haunted as if he hadn't had a proper night's sleep in years. He glared at me hatefully. "You think it's funny, peeping into people's rooms?"

I blinked. *What?*

"Don't you dare," Dad said before I could even think of opening my mouth, "I heard some fucking noises. And I saw you. You aren't getting out of this one."

And then, without another word, he began to hit me.

Immediately, I knew that this beating was different from the ones I had suffered before. I'd thought that I'd been familiar with my Dad's punches. But all those beatings from before were *nothing* when compared to this one. Dad exercised no restraint as he whaled on me, his knuckles driving into my body, breaking my skin.

Anger and confusion and hurt surged through me.

I could do nothing but stand there and take the punishment. I could do nothing but bear the pain.

At some point, Dad grabbed me and threw me on the ground. My back collided with the hard floor. I cried out as all the nerves in my spine ignited, sending a sharp, itching feeling all across my back. The only way I can properly describe the pain is that it was like the stinging tingle you get when accidentally touching steaming-hot water.

172

I honestly thought for a moment that I'd broken my spine. That I was on-track to becoming a paraplegic.

When I didn't get up, Dad rushed over to me. But not to help me back to my feet.

Instead, he kicked me while I was down—literally. He pounced on top of me, hitting me mercilessly. I tried to block Dad's fists from raining down on my face, but that only made him angrier.

That was the moment I broke. I cried out, my voice loud and cracking. Usually, crying made Dad hit harder, so I tried not to do it. But this time, I figured he was already hitting me as hard as he could. And God, it hurt so bad that I couldn't stop myself. I screamed in pain, my voice blindly searching the universe for help.

Blessedly, it worked.

Of all the people to come running in to save me, I least expected Kalisha. But there she suddenly was, grabbing my dad by the shoulder and yanking him off me. She was yelling, "Enough, Jamal! You're going to kill him!"

Her voice seemed to snap him out of it. He let her pull him away from me.

I didn't even move to get up and scramble away. I couldn't do anything but lay there in pain and sob.

Dully, I could make out Kalisha's voice as she talked to Dad about what had just happened. I only got bits and pieces of her words—but I knew that she was pissed. Dad had never beaten me so brutally before. I was so messed up looking that they'd have to call me out of school for the next few days.

After a few minutes, Kalisha seemed to remember that I was there getting blood on her bedroom carpet. She told me to wash off and then go back to bed. Even with her harsh tone, I couldn't bring myself to be angry at her. She'd just saved my life, for God's sake.

Had she not come to my rescue, Dad might've beaten me to death.

It was proof that she did have a heart. Or at least a conscience.

It took me a while to wash off. Everything hurt so bad—and even the warm water stung as I dabbed wads of damp toilet paper against my broken flesh. I could already see the beginnings of bruises forming all around my face and body.

When I laid back in bed, it was hard to fall asleep. Adrenaline was still shooting through my veins, and my body—despite its aches—was restless.

I cried quietly as I lay in my bed. I couldn't even look forward to the fact that I was going to get a few days off school, because it almost felt worse to have to be in my house with my dad. I even found myself wishing that Kalisha had been a little too late. That Dad *had* killed me.

Maybe then I'd be out of this pain that I was in. I could be up in Heaven with Mom.

Dad had always been a little paranoid. Even back when we'd lived in Virginia with Mom. As a kid, I used to believe him when he told me that people were out to get him. He used to feel along the walls of our house, claiming that he was checking for holes.

"That's how they get you, son," he'd claim, his eyes a little too wide. *"They drill holes in your walls to watch and listen to you. And then when they catch you slacking-,"* he made a cutting motion against his neck.

Eventually, I grew wise to his ramblings. The problem, I realized, wasn't that there were people out to get us. The problem was that my dad had a mental illness that had never been treated—and had been tolerated for so long by everyone around him that it had steadfastly become part of his unshakable reality.

I knew that this paranoia contributed to his constant belief that I was sneaking around and spying on him. For all I could tell, Dad might've even thought that I was a double-agent, working for some mysterious organization.

He probably didn't even realize that beating me was a bad thing. Maybe he found justice in it. Either way, he'd completely lost himself to his own warped version of reality.

And I was the one who had to suffer for it.

Chapter 22

"They're Mine, Nina"

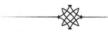

A few weeks after I'd been beaten within an inch of my life, Aunt Nina showed up on our doorstep to take Rhondelle back to Virginia with her.

As soon as I saw her, I ran into her arms. It had been a year since I'd last seen her—and I missed her like Hell.

She hugged me tightly. At first, I thought that she had come for all of us. But as soon as I pulled away and saw the sadness in her eyes, I knew that whatever truth came next would be bittersweet.

"I'm sorry," Nina mumbled. "We're just here for Rhondelle. Your Daddy isn't letting us take you and Wayne."

Even knowing this, Wayne and I begged Nina to take us anyways.

"I'm sorry," she kept saying. I knew that this was hurting her almost as much as it hurt us. "I wish I could."

As Rhondelle ran to pack up her things, Nina waited with us in the living room. Kalisha stood in the kitchen, just close enough to have us all within earshot and just far enough to not have to talk to Nina. She talked to Dad on speakerphone.

I listened to Dad's gruff voice explaining the situation. Rhondelle was going to be going back to Virginia to live with Nina. Wayne and I were to stay with him.

"If she tries to take those boys, I'll call the goddamn cops. You let her know that." Dad's voice came over the line. It sent a chill down my spine.

"Now, listen here." Nina had heard Dad's words just as well as I had. And she wasn't going to take them sitting down. She rose to her feet and marched over to the kitchen where Kalisha was. "I don't see why I can't take the boys. You keep complaining about having to feed them anyways."

"They're mine, Nina."

"How can you say that when you have to have this conversation with me over your girl's speakerphone? Those aren't your kids, Jamal. They're my *sister's* kids. And I want to take them."

"Fine, if you want me to file a kidnapping report."

I tried my hardest not to cry as Nina argued with Dad. I knew that her attempts were going to be fruitless. And even though it crushed me knowing that I wasn't going to be going back home to Virginia with Rhondelle, I knew that if I cried, I'd get in trouble as soon as Aunt Nina left. So, I stayed strong. And I pinched Wayne's leg so that he could stay strong, too.

After a little bit of back and forth, Dad hung up the phone and Nina stormed back into the living room. The conversation had not gone well. She crossed her arms.

"I'm sorry, baby. Your Daddy is too stubborn."

I knew for a fact that Nina wasn't afraid of the cops. If she could've, she would've snatched up all three of us regardless of what Dad threatened to do. But if the cops were called on Nina, there was a real chance that she'd have to turn Rhondelle back over to Dad and Kalisha. From her perspective, it was probably better to save one of us than none of us. I couldn't exactly argue with that logic.

Yet, I wasn't willing to go down without a fight.

"Aunt Nina, please." In my heart, I knew that begging wouldn't do anything. But I wanted to try anyways. I couldn't let this chance slip out of my grasp. Not until I knew I'd done everything to save myself. Unfortunately, with Kalisha's sharp ears just around the corner, I was limited in the things I could say. "Wayne and I are always getting in trouble here. Even for things that we don't do. I want to go home with you."

Nina looked heartbroken. And I hadn't even told her a fraction of the actual horrors that went on beneath Dad's roof.

But instead of whisking me away, she just gave me another tight hug and a kiss on the head. "I'm sorry. I'm sorry." She kept saying those words over and over. As if by repeating them, she could express just how truly apologetic she was.

I wasn't mad at Aunt Nina. I knew that she had fought for us. And as I saw the defeat in her eyes, I knew that there was no point in telling her about the beatings and the punishments. There was nothing that she could have done. And by telling her, I would've just made everything harder.

Rhondelle came out of her room with a single kid's sized suitcase at her hip and her schoolbag over her shoulders. I knew for a fact that she was leaving a lot of her belongings behind. She probably just wanted to get out of the house as fast as possible. I didn't exactly blame her.

Rhondelle shared a hug with Wayne and me. The last hug that all three of us would share for a long time.

Nina grabbed Rhondelle's suitcase. She got down on one knee to level with Wayne and me. "I'm not forgetting about you two," she promised. "I'm going to do everything in my power to get you two boys back to Virginia, okay?"

Even though I knew that it was a hopeless cause, I forced myself to smile for her sake. If nothing else, at least Rhondelle was getting out of Dad's house.

And then, she left. She smiled at us as she kissed us all goodbye, but I caught her crying as she walked down the driveway to her car. Seeing her like that broke my heart.

I couldn't understand why Dad was so fiercely adamant about keeping Wayne and me in his house. It wasn't like he *enjoyed* us there. It didn't even seem like he wanted us. So, why was he going through all the trouble to keep Aunt Nina from taking us?

Looking back on it, the answer was simple.

It was all about having control. Letting Aunt Nina know that whatever he said went. Dad was out to prove a point. And regardless of whether or not he succeeded, Wayne and I were going to suffer for it.

As I watched Aunt Nina's car pulling off down the street, taking one-third of us with her, I realized that nobody was coming to save Wayne and me. If we wanted to escape this house, we'd have to do it ourselves.

And that was exactly what I planned to do.

Chapter 23

RUN!

I didn't formulate my plan to run away from home overnight.

In fact, it was several nights before I even let myself seriously consider the notion alone. Running away seemed like the biggest betrayal that I could commit. And even though I feared and resented my father for all the pain that he had put me through—there was still a foolishly loving part of me that wanted to stay loyal to him.

Yet, once the thought entered my mind, it refused to let me go.

I'm pretty sure almost every kid thinks spitefully about running away from home once or twice. But very few kids are pushed to the point where they see it through. The illusory breaking point is never reached—and the "emergency" bookbag full of toys and pocket change is never put into action.

Except I *did* hit that point.

On the day I made my first attempt at running away, Dad wasn't home. I don't think I would've tried to make a break for it if he was.

I was serving out a punishment—squatting with the books. An old classic. Kalisha sat on the couch on the other side of the room, braiding Maya's hair. As she worked, she antagonized me. She joked that Dad had left for good this time. That he was out with another woman, and that he didn't care about any of us. That he probably wasn't going to come home. And even if he did, it sure as hell wouldn't be for any of us.

"You've been getting twitchy recently," Kalisha hummed, a *tsk*-ing quality to her tone. "I know that look. It's the same one your daddy gets before he's off 'working.'" She made indignant air quotes with her free hand. "Well, if you're going to run away, now's the time."

This was a trick. I knew it. With all my heart and soul, I knew that Kalisha wasn't *actually* telling me to run away.

Yet, the thought had been so persistent in my brain lately, so all-consuming, that I felt my legs begin to itch.

Stop it, I tried to will them back into submission. *Damn it, Feisal. You keep your ass right there. Stay put and squat with your damn books because this lady is setting you up.*

I looked at Kalisha's face, studying her expression.

I couldn't tell what she was thinking. So, she told me.

"Go ahead." Her voice was airy and dismissive. "I'm not going to stop you. And your daddy ain't here to stop you, either."

I still couldn't bring myself to move. I wanted to ask her if she was serious. But I wasn't supposed to talk while serving my punishment.

Kalisha's voice got harsher. More urgent. "You better go, boy. This is your only chance. Hurry up before I change my mind."

Kalisha rose to her feet. She mentioned something about needing more hairclips and wandered off down the hall to the bathroom.

It was then that I noticed Maya staring at me. I never thought much of my younger half-sister. She didn't encroach on my life like Cal did, and so she kind of just faded into the background most of the time. I knew that with Rhondelle gone, she was a little lonelier than usual. But I hadn't exactly been the most sympathetic to her plight. I figured that, like her brother, she was indifferent to me unless I was doing something for her.

Except the look in her eyes told me a different story.

Her big, brown eyes were wide and genuine. They looked almost anxious. They flickered from me to the door. At that moment, I knew what she was telling me without either of us having to utter a single word.

"Go. Before it's too late."

I sent a prayer up to the heavens. And then, I ran. I dropped my books, sprinting out the front door as fast as my legs could take me. The pads of my bare feet hit the sidewalk. Loose bits of gravel poked at my heels, but I barely cared.

After putting a few meters between myself and the house, I chanced a look back. Kalisha was standing there at the door, her arms crossed over her chest. She was making no move to come get me.

Despite that, I heard her calling after me, "Even I can run faster than that!"

I shook my head, brushing off her insult. *Free,* I realized. *I'm finally free!*

Once I knew that I was in the clear, running felt amazing. I felt like I was sprinting on the air. In a glorious version of heaven made up of pumping legs, thudding hearts, and rushing adrenaline. A song played in my head. I sang it as I ran, a giddy smile breaking on to my face.

"God, send me an angel from the heaves above/Send me an angel to heal my broken heart!"

I sang that line over and over again—a chorus of one.

Once or twice, I heard sirens. At first, I panicked, believing that Kalisha had called the police to collect me. But then the wailing sounds would pass, and I'd get back to running at full tilt.

Distance doesn't mean much to a kid. Even though I'd only been running for a few minutes, I was sure that if I kept going at my pace, I'd hit state lines by the time the sun went down. God, I could run all the way back to Virginia if I had to.

Yet, after about an hour, I began to lose steam.

I found myself at a languid pace. I hadn't eaten dinner, and hunger pangs gnawed at me. The sun had started its descent below the horizon. Under the shadow of dusk, the cop sirens became a little more frequent. Or, at least to *me,* they seemed to get more frequent.

Eventually, I got a little paranoid.

What if they *were* looking for me? Worse yet, what if they *caught* me?

I didn't want it to come to that. Plus, I figured that the later it got, the more dangerous it would be for me to be out and about. I didn't have a weapon on me to protect myself from kidnappers or muggers. I didn't even have any damn shoes.

With all this in my head, my next decision seemed rational.

I ran up to a house that looked vaguely familiar to me, and I knocked on the door. I figured that whoever was inside might be willing to room me for a night. At least until the sun came up again. Then, I could continue my escape in the morning.

A kid opened the door. She was a little younger than me and wore her hair in an assortment of beads and clips.

"Hey, Feisal." I recognized her voice. Her name was Abby, and she was one of Maya's friends. "What are you doing here?"

I didn't want to tell her the whole truth. So, as casually as I could, I replied, "I was just out running."

Abby's eyes flickered down to my bare feet. Then back up to my face.

"Anyways," I continued, trying to seem breezy and nonchalant (and probably failing), "I was wondering if I could stay over tonight. Just for a few hours. I can leave right in the morning. And if not, I can go to some other house and ask them."

"Um," Abby sucked in her cheeks. "Let me ask."

Abby left. She returned in a minute or two with an older woman who I assumed to be her grandmother. A look of concern drew itself across her face as she looked at me.

"What's going on here? Young man, where are your shoes?"

"They're at home," I said.

"Why aren't they on you?"

"I didn't have time to take them."

"And why not?"

I felt my heart beating in my chest. Why was she asking so many questions? She seemed like a nice enough woman—but I'd been burned so many times by now that trusting *anyone* felt like a gamble. Even so, I couldn't come up with a reasonable enough lie. And she was starting to look anxious.

So, I tried to tell the truth as candidly and as unremarkably as possible. "Well, I ran away from home. I didn't have a chance to get them before I made a break for it."

"Okay, well, why don't you come in?" She grabbed me by the shoulders and ushered me into her house.

Abby's grandmother's house was quaint. It reminded me a little bit of Mom's house in Virginia. The carpets were worn, but clean. The walls were adorned with adorably posed pictures of Abby. The smell of something warm and delicious radiated through the air.

Abby's grandmother invited me to dinner. If she was stressed having a strange little boy in her house, she certainly didn't show it. She set me a plate at the dinner table and served it with a fair helping of white rice, fried okra, and gumbo soup.

As we ate, she began to prod me for answers.

I was slow to talk at first, but eventually, I came out with the truth. "I ran away from home because I was being mistreated," I said, putting emphasis on the word *mistreated*, but not going into specifics about it. "I was actually wondering if you'd be able to call 9-1-1. Maybe they can help me."

A wrinkle creased on her forehead. "Well, if I were to do that, the police would probably either have to take you back home to your parents or take you to jail."

Maybe she thought this was some sort of *gotcha.* But I just shrugged.

"That's okay. I'd rather go to jail than be back home."

Abby and her grandmother both looked at me as though I'd lost my mind.

Eventually, Abby's grandmother did call the police. I guess my aversion to going home concerned her enough to take my request seriously. The police arrived as we were finishing up dinner.

The cop in charge was a big guy with a mustache and cold blue eyes. I couldn't read his expression as he looked me over. He asked me for my name and address, which I quickly provided.

"So, go over this with me, son. Why did you run away from home?"

"I'm being beat at home, sir. And I can't go home now, or I'll get into even more trouble than I'm already in." I relayed the day's earlier events to the officer. I told him how I'd been serving out a punishment. How Kalisha had practically given me *permission* to run away.

That part seemed to throw the cop off his balance. He questioned me further, but from that point on, I could start to hear inklings of disinterest in his voice. He didn't believe what I was saying was the truth.

After my questioning was over, he thanked Abby's grandmother for calling him. Then, he told me that I was coming with him.

"Are you going to take me to jail?" I asked.

He shook his head. "No, son. I'm taking you home." He motioned to his notepad, where he'd written down the address that I'd given him earlier.

I felt my stomach drop.

But it wasn't like I could do anything. He grabbed my arm. His grip was too strong for me to wriggle out of—and besides, it didn't seem wise to go against a police officer's wishes anyways. He put me in the back of his cop car and drove me back home to Chester Street. As we drove, I realized with a sinking sorrow how *little* of a distance I'd made it from my house.

When we pulled into the driveway, I could see Kalisha through the window. She was holding the phone up to her ear. She went a little rigid when she saw the police cruiser in her driveway. She muttered something over the line, then hung up. From her demeanor alone, I could tell that she had been talking to my dad.

The police officer parked his car and walked me up to the front door. As soon as Kalisha opened the door, the cop told me to go into the house. Kalisha smiled at me as I walked past her, the curve of her lips as cold and as cutting as a scythe. It was as though she'd known that I'd be right back.

Kalisha and the police officer talked for a while in private. I walked to my room, certain that I would be dead before daybreak after the stunt that I'd pulled. Cal seemed to agree with this belief. The first thing he said when I walked into our room was, "Feisal, you're probably the biggest idiot in the world."

"You're the only idiot here," I snapped back. "Mind your business."

Cal's eyes narrowed. I knew already that he'd be reporting my callous words to his mother. I couldn't care less. I was already in trouble for running away. What was one more little infraction going to do? It was just another nail in my already sealed coffin.

I caught Wayne's gaze, and I knew that we were both thinking the same thing about me.

Dead man walking.

"Just wait until your daddy gets home," Cal taunted. "He's going to kill you."

Grimacing, I lay down in my bed. I didn't doubt it.

Chapter 24

"KIDDIE JAIL"

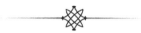

The Brookstone Center for Juveniles was smack-dab in the middle of nowhere. I assumed that its remoteness helped with deterring runaways.

It was oddly fitting, seeing as I was being sent there as a direct result of the whole *running away from home* stunt I'd pulled two weeks earlier.

As expected, Dad had been furious when he finally came back from his shit on the road. I was given the usual punishments—beatings and being forced to squat—but Dad had also apparently come to the conclusion that I was too troubled to continue serving out my sentences at home, where I might poison Cal or Maya or Wayne with my delinquent tendencies.

So, I was being sent to Brookstone.

Dad made it seem like it was going to be one step lower than Alcatraz. But all the promotional brochures that I'd peeked at made it look more like a hospital of sorts.

On the Saturday that I was to be admitted, Dad and I made the long drive up through the mountains to get there. Nerves and excitement coursed through me. Dad had intended for Brookstone to be a punishment—but I was ecstatic to be getting away from home. This was what I'd wanted all along, after all.

I just couldn't believe that it was actually happening.

I sent a prayer up to the heavens for Wayne. With me gone, he was going to have to bear the brunt of the pain under Dad's roof. I felt a little guilty for leaving him. I wished that he could come with me.

But as Dad ranted about Brookstone to me, I was starting to feel grateful that he was at home.

"They'll break you down, man," Dad snapped. "Expect cold showers and stale, moldy food. Prison slop. This isn't a vacation."

I tuned him out. He was just trying to scare me. At least, that's what I wanted to believe.

Brookstone wasn't an ordinary facility. And it wasn't a prison like Dad had made it out to seem. The facility was actually a set of two huge cabins—one for administration, and one for rooming. They were connected in the middle. Trees surrounded the facility. Beyond them was a large gate that ran along the perimeter of the property.

The owners of this place must be white, I thought. The place reminded me of camping and hiking which, at the time, was a sport I thought only white people engaged in.

Walking into the lobby, I did not see anything that reminded me of prison. Instead, the employees were friendly, and the facility was clean. The secretary checked me in. Shortly after, Dad left. He didn't say much to me as he went. He didn't hug me or tell me that he'd be back for me soon.

His parting words were a single command, "Don't cause any trouble."

I nodded, feeling an invisible weight coming off my shoulders as Dad left.

A few minutes later, I was taken into a back room, where a counselor asked me a series of questions. The counselor was a small woman with round glasses. Her tone was gentle but professionally distant as she asked me all about my home life and my mental health.

I tried answering honestly.

Even though I was glad to be away from my horrible home, I still didn't have much of a will to live. And I harbored a lot of anger toward my family for the things that they had put me through. I wanted terrible things to happen to Dad, Kalisha, and Kalisha's kids.

Usually, I tried to tone down my resentment when I talked about my family. But in front of this counselor, I was honest.

"I'd rather be with Mom than go back to that house," I said, my eyes firmly on the floor.

"My records say that your mother is-,"

"She's dead."

"So, are you saying that you'd rather be dead than at home?" The counselor tilted her head a little.

I clenched my jaw. "Yes. That's what I'm saying."

"And you'd like for bad things to happen to your father, your father's girlfriend, and her two children?" She confirmed.

I nodded. "Especially Cal."

"And Cal is the boy?"

"Yeah."

The counselor knitted her brows together. As if she couldn't quite understand the things that I was telling her. "Why do you want bad things to happen to your family, Feisal?"

"Those jerks aren't my family," I said instantly. I talked about the things that went on in my father's house. The beatings. The blamings. The fact that my Dad had forced Wayne and I to fight each other like dogs for his own enjoyment.

As I spoke, I noticed the counselor jotting things down in her notebook. Yet, I could tell that she was writing selectively. Her pen would pause whenever I spoke about being beaten, then resume its scratching when I talked about wanting to die or wishing misfortune upon Dad and Kalisha and Cal.

194

Why isn't she writing down everything? I wondered. I figured that maybe this was just how they did it at this facility. Maybe the counselors had an obligation to jot down certain notes and not others.

Either way, I forced myself not to focus too much on her notetaking.

Once I'd finished talking, she spoke. "Well, thank you for opening up to me about all of that. It must've been very difficult." She cleared her throat. "In any case, let me brief you a bit on what you can expect moving forward. First, you'll be on a three-day watch for suicidal ideation."

I blinked. I had no idea what that even meant. "Okay."

"You'll need to surrender your shoes, shoestrings, and anything else on your person that might be used as a weapon to harm yourself or others. Your clothes will be initialed so that they do not get confused with anyone else's. And your full schedule will be delivered to you as soon as you're settled into your room."

I nodded, accepting all of this.

The counselor collected my shoes and personal items. Then, she led me to an elevator, and we rode up to the Adolescent Ward, where I'd be staying. As soon as I stepped off the elevator, I was bombarded by an explosion of noise.

Kids yelling. Kids screaming. Kids running down the halls, behind chased by frazzled-looking employees.

One kid sitting in the lounge area was cursing out a staff member. And to my shock, the staff member was swearing right back at the kid.

I bristled. I'd never been around so many disrespectful kids in my life. My confidence in the quality of life that I'd have at Brookstone wavered a little.

What the hell have I gotten myself into?

The counselor seemed completely unbothered. She took me into my room, which was essentially just a small box with two beds, a pair of nightstands, a storage shelf, and a small connecting bathroom. Only one of the beds was made up. A small window peered out over the grounds.

The counselor gave me a gray kidney-shaped basin full of hygiene products, a towel, and shower slippers. I also received a toothbrush, toothpaste, and a packet of Vaseline for my lips.

Then, the counselor left me to get settled in.

I'm certain that this kind of experience is scary for a lot of kids. But for me, it was nothing short of paradise. Having been used to living in a noisy house without a lick of personal space or privacy, the fact that I had an entire room and bathroom to myself was the peak of luxury.

After about fifteen minutes, one of the staff members came into my room. I tried to figure out what her role was, but I couldn't ascertain that from her badge alone. It just had her first name in tiny black letters and then the word *STAFF* printed beneath.

I never learned the actual titles of any of the staff members. All I knew was that they were around to make sure that we kids behaved, participated in activities, and did not kill each other or ourselves. Staff carried keys and a radio, but nothing else.

The staff member gave me two pieces of paper—one with a list of all the activities for the week, and the other with a menu on it. Outside my door, I could see the other kids gathering up for dinner.

I stood up to join them, but a look from the staff member sat me back down.

"Sorry, Feisal. You can't go this time. You're on watch for the next 72 hours. Per the doctor's orders, you'll be spending the next three days in your room." She chewed on the inside of her cheek. "As soon as your watch period is over, you'll be free to join the others in activities and meals. But for right now, this is what's best for your health. It won't be so bad, though. The time will be up before you know it."

I nodded. As the staff member had been talking, I'd pieced together what the first counselor had been talking about when she'd mentioned a *three-day watch period for suicidal ideation.* They were worried that I was going to try to kill myself.

I could've spoken up and insisted that even though I wanted to die, I wasn't exactly planning to do the deed myself. But the idea of spending the next three days alone didn't sound half bad. I'd have time to myself for once. Time to think and reflect on everything.

I put my dinner order in with the staff member, and a short time later, she returned with my food.

I was startled when I saw it. It was a full-course meal, complete with an entrée, sides, dessert, juice, water, and milk. I honestly couldn't remember the last time I'd had a dinner so complete or filling.

As I ate, for the first time in a long time, I felt my spirits lifting. Even if just a little.

My isolation went by quickly.

Staff came in and out of my room semi-frequently, trying their best to ensure that I wasn't too bored. They brought me a lot of coloring pages and crayons to pass the time. Those coloring pages quickly became one of my favorite parts of the whole ordeal.

I don't know what about them was so appealing, but I was hooked. I asked for coloring pages all day, every day—even after my isolation period was over. I saved every single one that I finished. Some of them, I'd give away to my favorite staff members or peers.

Eventually, I became so insistent with my requests for more coloring pages, that the staff allowed me to make my own copies. I think they were a little exasperated by my constant requests, and I was well-behaved enough to be trusted with the copy machine.

Every time I was in the activity room, I'd look through the coloring books that they had available. If I found a picture I liked, I'd promptly take it to the copy room to make a copy for myself. I never copied sad or negative pictures. I only wanted the happy-looking ones. Sometimes, I'd add to them if I felt they needed something. A scene at the park might warrant a brighter sun or a few extra clouds. And, like any artist, I made sure to sign my work when it was finished.

At one point, my collection was about as thick as a phone book. Maybe even a little thicker. I have no idea why I loved coloring so much. Maybe it was simply because the act of bringing a picture to life gave me joy.

Every so often, staff did a random room check for contraband.

Back then, I had no idea what the hell a *contraband* was. I thought that it was an actual item—and not a category of stuff.

Staff would do their rounds, slipping in and out of each room and shuffling through people's closets. Some kids screamed at the staff in protest. Others just stood back, waiting for it to be over.

When it was my turn to have my room checked, I wasn't worried. I knew that the staff wouldn't find contraband, because all I had were my personal things and my coloring pages.

The staff member who searched my room was a short white woman. She looked angry. I could tell that she hated this particular chore of hers. Or maybe she was just annoyed that she had to come to work every day just to deal with a bunch of troubled kids that weren't her own.

When she found my mountain of coloring pages, she paused.

"Why do you have so many of these?" she asked, eyes narrowing.

"My coloring pages?" I shrugged. "I don't know. I like them."

She shook her head. "I'm going to have to take these. You can keep three at a time."

I frowned. "Really? But the staff lets me keep them."

I'm sure there was an ulterior motive for this woman's suspicion. It was possible that she figured that I was hoarding the pages in order to Ethan Hunt some sort of troublemaking scheme. It must've been incomprehensible that a boy my age would care so much about coloring sheets.

But one good look at the sheets would've told her otherwise. Who spends so much time making a scheme look beautiful?

Either way, she apparently didn't want to clue me in to her suspicions. She just dismissively said, "It's not fair to the others that you're keeping them all to yourself."

"Nobody else really cares about them," I insisted, feeling my neck prickle as the woman bunched up a stack of my pages. "If they wanted their own, they could ask the staff for copies like I did."

She didn't have another reasonable excuse. She didn't try to find one. "Sorry," she said. She scooped up all but three drawings at the bottom of the stack. Then, she left.

I was appalled. *Why the hell does she care so much about a couple of drawings?* It wasn't like I was storing food or plastic knives in my room.

Later, at dinner, I convened with my usual group. Since the lifting of my 72-hour watch period, I'd been allowed to join the normal activities, including meals with my peers. I'd found a small group of kids that I liked. My pool of friends to choose from wasn't too broad, though. Because of what I'd said during intake, I was separated into a smaller cohort. We weren't allowed to talk or be near any of the other kids.

That didn't stop us from trying, though. Especially me. I've always been friendly. I waved and smiled at anyone even remotely pleasant that I passed, regardless of whether I was supposed to.

When I told my friends at dinner what had happened with my confiscated coloring pages, they couldn't make sense of it, either.

One kid just shrugged. "It's what they do here. Could be worse, Feisal."

Sighing, I nodded. It was hard to disagree with him on that one.

Every day, I had to attend group therapy, or "group" for short. In group, all the kids from my cohort joined together in the activities room with a counselor. We'd all pull up a chair and sit in a circle.

Group started with introductions. We'd all say our names and why we'd been put into the facility. We did this ritual every single time just in case there were any newcomers. All the kids pretty much said the same things when it was their turn.

"I was disrespecting my parents."

"I got into a fight at school."

"I stole from a Dollar Tree."

When it was my turn, I'd tell everyone that I was there because I'd run away from home. The counselor would remind me to elaborate. He'd ask me *why* I'd run away from home.

I always hated this part. I hated having to tell all of these kids that my dad and his girlfriend had beaten me severely. That the only contingency plan I'd been able to devise had been running away. After disclosing this, I always kept my eyes on the tile floor until the next kid had finished his introduction. I never wanted to see the reactions my story had gotten from the counselor or my peers.

As the rest of the kids talked about their experiences, I found myself wondering how many of them were like me. How many were being beaten or abused at home? How many were here because they were *actually* just troublemakers?

On top of group, I met with a family doctor every week. Our meetings were only about twenty minutes and were much more clinical than my group sessions. The doctor would basically just go down a laundry list of questions.

"Are you having any suicidal thoughts? How do you feel about your dad? How do you feel about his girlfriend? How are you sleeping at night? Are you ready to go home?"

No matter what I said, the doctor reacted with flat disaffection. It was like she was just doing the bare minimum for her job instead of really listening to me. I tried to talk to her about my dad and Kalisha. I tried to explain in my best words how they threatened me, beat me, and how the overall environment at our house was the very definition of unsafe. I tried to insist that going back there would put my life at risk.

The doctor usually responded to all of this by trying to up my medication dosage.

Then, the doctor would tell me my discharge date, and my stomach would sink. I tried not to think about that dreadful day—the one where I'd be forced to leave the facility and go back home. When I talked to my friends, they all seemed excited about their discharge dates. They wanted to go back to the real world. To see their friends. Maybe even to see their families.

But for me, it seemed like a death sentence. Every time I even thought about being sent home, my heart would thump out of my chest—as if I was being chased by a serial killer or something.

The only person I even wanted to see was Wayne. Not a day had gone by that I wasn't worried about how he was doing. I prayed that Cal, Kalisha, and Dad had taken some mercy on my little brother.

Still, my worry for him wasn't enough for me to want to go back. I tried everything I could to stay at the facility. I told as many staff members and counselors as I could about my home life, hoping that one of them would do something to intervene.

Quickly, though, I learned that intervention wasn't going to happen. Some of the counselors heard me out, but all they were able to provide me with was their support and some well-meaning advice. Most of the counselors didn't believe me and weren't shy about showing their incredulity. They'd either make excuses for Dad and Kalisha, or they'd blame me for everything that was happening.

"I know it can be hard when someone you love passes away," they'd always say, passing the buck to my grief over my dead mother, "but acting out isn't a solution."

They all thought that I was some kid who was simply struggling to cope with the loss of his mother—rather than a kid who had gotten salt poured into his wounds by being abused rather than comforted after his mother's death.

The day before I was to be discharged, I grew desperate and threw a tantrum.

It was completely unlike me. I'd never acted out like this before. Especially not at the facility. I didn't know if it would help or hurt my case. I was just hoping that if I threw a big enough fit, I'd be deemed *"not ready for discharge."*

I trashed my room. I tore my linens off my bed, my clothes off my shelves, and emptied my hygiene products onto the floor. I kicked and punched my pillows.

When the staff did their rounds and found my room in its haphazard state, however, they simply smiled at me and politely told me to make sure I had everything cleaned before lunchtime.

"What if I don't do it?" I asked indignantly.

The staff member sighed. "Then you'll really be inconveniencing the cleaner on her rounds." Then, the staff member walked off to the next room.

Well, that didn't work, I thought, thoroughly vexed.

As a last-ditch attempt at saving myself, I snuck off to the nurse's desk after lunch. I thought that if I told her everything, she'd have to stop them from sending me home. I don't know why I assumed this would work. I'd told so many of the staff members my story now, only for most of them to dismiss me. Yet, I didn't want to lose hope.

When I told the nurse, I made it my mission to be as explicit as possible about what went on in my household. I talked about being forced to fight Wayne. About being held down by Dad so that Cal could beat me up. About Dad nearly punching me to death. I must've looked crazy. But I didn't care. I was desperate.

To the nurse's credit, she did seem genuinely disturbed by my story. She told me to go back to my room, and that someone would be there to talk to me in a few minutes. I did as I was told, and about an hour later, a staff member popped into my room to hand down my verdict.

"Three days," she said. "That's how long your stay is being extended for."

Three days. It wasn't the injunction I'd hoped for, but it was a small blessing. I sighed. I would take it.

Chapter 25

WHAT GOES ON IN MY HOUSE STAYS IN MY HOUSE

*E*ven though I knew what was waiting for me at home, I tried to believe that things would be different this time around. Everyone at the facility seemed to believe that my life was going to change for the better after my treatment. I wanted to trust them.

But unfortunately, and expectantly, nothing really changed.

In fact, if anything *did* change, it was that my brother and I were being treated *worse* than usual. Dad and Kalisha fought almost every single day. And, of course, they took out their anger from those fights on us.

I don't even know why they argued so much. Maybe it was that my dad was home more often lately, and so they had more opportunities to be at one another's throats. Maybe they just weren't getting along anymore.

Another thing that changed was that now, Wayne and I were sharing the burden of the punishments more equally. As I'd feared would happen, Dad must've gotten a little more comfortable beating on Wayne during my stay at the facility. That habit didn't dry up after I'd come home.

At one point, Dad brought home a litter of puppies that had been given to him by one of his work buddies. Kalisha threw a fit about the dogs. She didn't want any "dirty animals" in her house. They argued for a few hours, then slept in separate rooms.

By the next afternoon, the puppies were gone.

I never found out what happened to the dogs. But I do know that Wayne was blamed for their disappearance. Dad accused Wayne of killing them—completely disregarding the fact that Wayne had never killed anything larger than a potato bug in his life.

The way Dad punished poor Wayne; you would've thought that he'd loved those puppies all his life instead of less than forty-eight hours.

Dad claimed later that he knew it was Wayne who had gotten rid of the puppies because he'd "heard" him through the walls.

Dad was starting to hear things more often. Even then, I knew that his paranoia was worsening. I hated being in rooms with him. Even more than that, I hated being in rooms *alone* with him. I think everybody else in the house mostly felt the same way.

At one point, Dad and I were driving in his truck. We were out to go grab something from the hardware store—a pipe had broken in the house, and Kalisha was determined not to let us rest until it was fixed.

I had hoped that the drive would be quiet. Maybe Dad and I could just listen to the radio together, and instead of conversation, we could just quietly bob our heads to the music. But Dad wasn't interested in that kind of drive. As soon as we hit the main street, he started talking.

"You know they sent an agent to our house?" Dad asked.

I blinked. "What?"

"Because you were running your mouth at the facility."

Oh. So, that's what the extended stay was for. I shook my head, feigning obliviousness. "No. They did?"

Dad nodded stiffly. "Listen and listen good, Feisal. What goes on in my house *stays* in my house. Those people don't care about you. They aren't going to save you. Hell, most of them don't even like their jobs." He laughed, sharp and angry.

I clenched my teeth. I knew that Dad was lying. Or maybe he wasn't lying. But he certainly didn't know the truth. Yes, there were a lot of counselors at the facility who seemed tired and uninterested in us kids. But there were also some staff members who genuinely liked working with us.

It was starting to dawn on me that maybe Dad didn't know *half* of what he was always talking about.

A thought occurred to me. *What if I could have a regular conversation with him again? Maybe I could tell him how I really feel.*

The thought was terrifying. But it seemed worth a shot. Maybe Dad just needed some perspective.

"Dad," I said, my voice a little shaky. "Do you like us?"

The question slipped. I had been thinking about it, but I hadn't meant to ask it. And now, it was out in the air between us.

I regretted my words instantly.

What the hell was I thinking, asking my Dad that?

Dad side-eyed me. "What the hell are you talking about?"

I didn't say anything. I didn't want to dig an even deeper hole for myself to crawl out of.

Dad didn't take my silence kindly. "Feisal, what the fuck are you talking about? Do I like *who?*" He reached over and grabbed me by the shirt. His other hand gripped the wheel tightly, knuckles paling. "I'm not asking you again."

I looked straight ahead; my spine suddenly ramrod straight.

"I was just—I just wanted to know if you still liked Wayne and I," I stammered. Once the words came out, I couldn't stop them. "I remember when you were nice to us. Like, back before..." *Back before Mom died,* my inner voice supplied. "...I remember when you'd come back home after a week on the road. You and I would go fishing and we'd have fun together. But we haven't gone fishing in forever, and so, I was just sort of wondering-,"

"Feisal, you sound so goddamned stupid right now. Do you hear yourself?" Dad snapped. He let go of my shirt. As he drove, he quietly mocked me under his breath, *"We used to go fishing. You liked us back then."*

I bowed my head in shame. I couldn't even blame Dad for his reaction. I felt so stupid and humiliated for having spoken those words to him. Quietly, I vowed not to ever ask him anything like that ever again.

Honestly, it was pointless to ask my dad questions that I already knew the answer to.

Chapter 26

D.H.S

*I*f I get on the wrong bus, maybe I'll get lost.

The thought terrified me, but not for the typical reasons. Most people do not hope to wind up lost and far away from home. But to me, the idea of it seemed enticing. I figured that if I "accidentally" took the wrong bus coming home from school, it would give me a good excuse to get away from my house.

No, the reason that thought scared me was because I had briefly inherited a touch of my father's neuroses and was worried that someone might be reading my mind and would get me in trouble for even *thinking* up such a plot.

But, as with most of my plans to run away from home, this one stuck with me as viable. And that meant it was hard to get out of my head.

I carried out my idea after school one day. The bell had just rang, and my classmates were running to the back doors of the building where the busses loaded up for their daily drop-offs. Usually, I dragged my feet when school was dismissed. I wasn't exactly eager to leave the safe haven of school for the Hell of home.

But on that day, I briskly made my way out with everyone else. Scenarios raced through my head as I walked as confidently as I could toward the bus at the back of the line. The bus that was farthest away from the one that usually took me.

My heart thudded in my chest as I boarded the bus. I kept my head down as I passed by the driver. She was distracted by the bus radio and didn't notice that I wasn't one of her usual drop-offs.

I sat in the back, keeping my head low as I peered out my window.

I kept waiting for someone to tap my shoulder. For one of my classmates to loudly declare, "Feisal, you're not usually on this bus!"

But nobody did. Most of the other kids on the bus left me alone—too busy talking to their friends or listening to music to be concerned about my presence. As the buses began to pull out of the drive, I felt my heart dip.

This is it.

At first, I was thrilled. My plan had worked! But as the bus drove further and further away from my neighborhood, I began to get worried. I didn't realize how far this bus drove out of town. And even though that had been my intention from the start, it still concerned me that I was being taken so far away.

As the bus went through each of its stops, more and more kids stepped off. Until finally, there was just me and one other kid on the bus.

The bus driver stopped in front of a blue house, and the other kid stood up to get off.

When the bus driver turned to say goodbye to him, her eyes narrowed as she caught my figure in her rearview mirror. It had taken her entire route, but finally, the bus driver noticed my existence and realized that I wasn't supposed to be there.

When she questioned me, I came up with a lie on the spot. I told her that I was taking her bus today instead of my usual one because I was supposed to be going over to my grandmother's house after school. Coincidentally, I added, my grandmother's house was on this stop.

The bus driver's eyes narrowed, but I apparently looked honest enough. Slowly, she nodded, accepting my story.

Not wanting to clue her in to the fact that I was lying through my teeth, I threw my backpack around my shoulders and stood up. As confidently as I could, I disembarked from the bus. Slowly, I walked toward one of the nearby houses.

I was hoping that the bus driver would simply peel away—as the bus often did after dropping me off at my dad's house—but apparently, this driver wasn't entirely buying my story and wanted to make sure that I was going where I'd claimed.

Realizing that there was no way out of the hole I'd dug myself into, I climbed up the porch steps of a house with a blue roof. My palms sweated as I knocked on the front door. Blood rushed in my ears. *What was going to happen when the door opened? Would the bus driver realize that I'd lied to her?*

The front door opened, and an older-looking woman peered out. She blinked in confusion as she looked at me, but smiled regardless.

"Why, hello, young man. What can I help you with?" she asked.

Apparently, the sight of the woman had convinced the bus driver of my honesty. I heard the rev of an engine as the bus kicked back into gear and pulled away.

Feeling slightly more at ease, I decided to continue with my mission of escaping home. I smiled up at the lady as politely as I could and told her candidly that I had taken the wrong bus home on purpose so that I could get myself lost.

Her brows knit slightly. "Now, why would you want to do that?"

"I don't want to go home, ma'am," I said. Then, as if realizing that this woman might not realize the validity of my statement (after all, as mentioned earlier, almost every kid wants to run away from home at least once in their lives), I also told her about the abuse that I was facing at the hands of my father and his girlfriend.

The woman's eyes widened, and she ushered me into her house immediately.

There were five kids in the house already—probably the woman's *actual* kids or grandkids. The oldest one was about my age. I didn't recognize any of them from school.

The woman introduced herself as Marie. After warning the other kids that they needed to have their homework done by dinnertime, she pulled me into the kitchen. Marie poured us both a glass of water, and we sat down at the table to talk more about my situation.

The more I described to Marie, the more concerned she became. The space between her forehead creased as I talked about my father forcing Wayne and me to fight and about the recent debacle concerning my dad's unfounded belief that Wayne had killed the litter of puppies.

"That's terrible. Just terrible," Marie kept saying.

My experiences affected her deeply. She was sad that I'd had to endure my household, and she even spoke about wanting to keep me under her roof with her kids. Eventually, unsure of what to do with me, she called a friend over. That friend suggested calling the DHS.

When I gave the friend a nervous and confused look, she clarified, "Social services, honey."

Both Marie and her friend were kindhearted women—but both were concerned that they'd get in trouble for quartering me in their house.

216

"It could be considered kidnapping," Marie's friend had reasoned.

That was a fair enough point.

At her friend's instruction, Marie called the DHS. The operator told Marie that the DHS would be over to her house soon to investigate—and warned her to make sure I stayed put until then. Not exactly a difficult chore—I wasn't itching to leave or anything.

As the sun went down, Marie plated up dinner for us all. She didn't make a big deal out of my presence at all. She just made an extra serving for me and treated it like it was the most normal thing in the world.

I wouldn't mind living with a nice woman like her, I thought idly.

By the time dinner was over and the sun had fallen below the horizon, I'd almost completely forgotten about the DHS having been called.

But then, inevitably, the officers arrived. The DHS officers pulled into Marie's driveway in a plain black sedan. When they got out of their vehicle, I took stock of them. There were two of them, both women. One tall and one short.

Retrospectively, I'd say the tall one looked a lot like *Shay Kool Lay Lay,* one of the drag queens from RuPaul's Drag Race. She was pretty, with a short-cropped haircut and sharp cheekbones. The shorter one looked like a slightly less bullish and black version of Miss Trunchbull. She wore her hair in cornrows.

The two DHS officers introduced themselves to Marie (their names escaped me). They seemed sweet as they talked to Marie and Marie's friend, insisting that they were going to do everything in their power to protect me.

Marie gave me a warm hug before sending me off with them.

I walked with Tall and Short back to their sedans, feeling confident that my plan to run away from home had been a stellar success.

Boy, was I in for a shock.

As soon as the car doors closed, all the warmth in the DHS officers' faces vanished. Tall sat behind the wheel, putting the car in gear and backing out of Marie's driveway. Short turned to glare at me from the passenger's seat.

In a flash, the two sweet DHS officers had turned right into what I liked to call *woollies.*

"Boy, what the hell are you doing way over here? Your family is looking for you," Short snapped. "We should take your little ass to jail since you want to keep running away from home."

Crap. Dad and Kalisha *had* been looking for me, then. And if that was the case, it meant that whatever awaited me at home was likely going to be a punishment worse than death—if not death itself.

I didn't respond. I just sat there, terrified.

"Well?" Tall asked. "What do you have to say to that?"

I stammered out a response. I tried to tell the DHS officers what I'd told Marie. But my nerves scrambled up my words, and my story didn't stick its landing nearly as well as it had at Marie's house.

As I spoke, Tall just laughed.

Short shook her head. "You ain't getting abused. You just don't want to get your ass beat. That's what's wrong with kids these days."

"Don't I know it," Tall agreed.

What I wouldn't give to have us trade places for a day, I thought bitterly, as Tall and Short drove me back to my house.

These women didn't see a kid who needed help. They just saw another Black kid that needed to be punished and put in his place. They treated me like a criminal for the entire agonizing car ride, taunting me. They told me that if I ran away again, they'd arrest me and take me to jail.

I thought that Tall and Short would take me straight home. Instead, they took me to the DHS office. Tall escorted me into a room that had a bunch of cubicles. I was told to wait at one of the cubicle desks until they finished up my case report. Then, they'd take me home.

As I waited, I felt this terrible sense of defeat wash over me. There were about a dozen DHS officers in the room that I was in. All of them stared at me, but not one of them made a move to help me. Nobody even asked me if I wanted a glass of water or anything.

I'd always had a pretty decent sense of hope. But sitting there, being pointedly ignored by the very agency that had been put in place to help kids like me—it made me realize that authority was not to be trusted. Furthermore, the way Tall and Short had treated me had ruined my perception of Black female authority figures.

I'd always tried my best to respect women. Especially with how much I loved and respected my mom. But my interaction with those two awful DHS officers left a sour taste in my mouth. One that I regretfully still have to some degree to this day.

They had the opportunity to help me. And they'd turned me away. I'm sure that they were raised the "old-fashioned way." The way that said that what happened in a Black household *stayed* in a Black household. The way that said Black boys were supposed to act a certain way, live a certain way, and suffer a certain way.

Would things have been different, I wondered, if I were a girl? Or if I were white?

I didn't know. I still don't.

After an hour of waiting at the DHS office, Tall and Short drove me back to my house. Tall knocked on my front door, and Dad answered it. Kalisha was right behind him. Tall and Short talked to Dad and Kalisha congenially, as if they were all the best of friends.

"Your son made some accusations, so unfortunately, we're going to have to question some of the other children in your house. I hate to do this, but it's procedure."

"I understand," Dad said. "Give me a second, I'll round them up for you."

Dad grabbed me by the shoulder and harshly took me back to my room. He opened the door, throwing me inside. Wayne and Cal were already settled in for the night. They were sitting on their beds.

"Wayne, Cal. Some ladies want to talk to you," Dad said. His voice was tight. He narrowed his eyes. "Don't say anything stupid. Do you understand me?"

Wayne and Cal exchanged a look. Then, they turned back to Dad and nodded.

I knew then not to expect anything. If Wayne and Cal had told the truth that night, we probably all would've been taken out of the house. But because both were too afraid to cross Dad for the consequences such an act of betrayal might bring, neither was going to back me up.

After Wayne and Cal were questioned, Dad and Kalisha talked a little longer with the DHS workers. Eventually, the DHS workers left.

That's it. I'm dead, I took a shaky breath, settling in for the long night of punishment that surely awaited me.

Except nothing especially bad happened.

Dad peeked into our room, but only to glare at me. He pointed a furious finger in my direction. "Nobody is going to save you, Feisal. You saw how those women acted, didn't you? They don't give a damn about you. Nobody does." He smiled cruelly. "No matter how many times you try to run away, no matter how many people you beg for help, you will always end up right back here. Under *my* roof. Do you understand me?"

I wanted to protest. I wanted to fight back. I wanted to tell Dad that if I could just get the right person to listen, then I would be able to make him eat his words.

But the thing was, I couldn't help but accept that what my father said was *right.* Why did I have any right to believe that somebody would save me when the world was insistent on proving the opposite?

So, I didn't say anything.

Dad just shook his head. He laughed humorlessly. "Yeah. That's what I thought."

Chapter 27

A NORMAL CHRISTMAS

My first Christmas at the Chester Street house was a landmark one for a few reasons. Predominantly, it was the first Christmas that I spent without my mom, and at the same time it was the first Christmas that I spent *with* my dad.

We didn't think that he'd make it home. He had a last-minute holiday job to do. But miraculously, he was able to finish the job early. He made it in late at night on Christmas Day, holding a big pile of presents for all of us.

My relationship with Dad had withered away to nothing at that point, but I was still somewhat excited to see him on such an important holiday. Wayne and I were gifted a puzzle kit. The puzzle kit was three-dimensional, and once completed, would look like a toy truck. Cal got a few *Dragonball*-themed toys. Maya got a makeup kit.

It was a shockingly normal day. Nobody was punished, and everybody got along.

Even so, I had a little charge of anxiety running through me for most of the night. I was always a little antsy when perfect moments like this happened. Even though I wanted nothing more than for the peace to go on forever, it felt sometimes like we were all just killing time until the other shoe dropped. Until something pissed off Dad or Kalisha, and we were punished.

This time, I tried to force away the feeling. I tried to enjoy the lack of stress. The genuine joy that everyone around me was experiencing. It almost felt like being in a normal blended household with a normal family.

Looking at Cal and Wayne as they showed each other their gifts, I thought wistfully, *Wow, it must be nice to feel like this all the time. No problems. Stress-free. Not having to feel like you're walking on thin ice.*

This Christmas will always stick out in my memory as one of the few good days I ever had while living with Dad and Kalisha.

It was little sparks of joy like this one that kept me hoping and praying that things would change someday. These moments kept me on the hook of a promise. They taunted me with a ghostly vision of the life I could've led if things were different.

But I wasn't stupid. Maybe the camel's back wouldn't break tonight. But in a few days, it would snap. Just like it always did.

Just like it always would.

Chapter 28

THE BETRAYAL OF JACK

*A*fter a particularly gruesome punishment, I came to school with a knife.

I wasn't going to hurt anyone with it. Honestly, I wasn't. But I knew that with my track record, bringing a knife to school would guarantee me another stay at a behavioral health facility. And I needed to get out of Dad's house, ASAP.

I don't even remember what had brought about the punishment. But Dad had apparently gotten tired of his typical standard beatings and had decided to shake things up a little by tying me up and throwing me in the laundry room for hours.

The entire experience had been miserable. He'd tied the ropes so tightly that they bit into my flesh. He'd locked me in the dark room. I wasn't allowed to eat dinner. And that was *after* having beaten me for several minutes.

So, I brought a knife to school. As I'd hoped and expected, I was immediately referred to another behavioral facility for troubled kids.

This facility was a different one than the facility I'd been at previously. Instead of a cabin-styled place in the middle of nowhere, this facility was smack-dab in the middle of one of the busiest streets in Arkansas.

I'd actually seen the building several times during drives. It was nondescript. Tall and boxy and constructed out of tan bricks. I'd assumed that it was just some random business or something.

The check-in process was a lot more thorough than it had been at the first facility. The doctor who did my intake was an older man. He was a bit on the heavy side, but he was well-dressed and held himself with quiet confidence. His name was Dr. Jenson.

When Dr. Jenson spoke to me, it felt like he was actually listening to what I had to say. When he took notes, he wasn't selective about what parts of my story to keep and discard. He wrote down all of it.

I explained the same thing to him that I'd explained to everyone else. At this point, I'd retold my horrific stories so many times that it was almost boring. Still, despite the redundancy, I knew that disseminating this information properly was important.

"So, what steps have you taken so far to try and remove yourself from the situation?" Dr. Jenson asked.

I was flabbergasted. I'd never been asked that before. Hope budding in my chest for the first time in a long time,

I said, "I've done a few things. I've tried to report it. I've tried to run away. Nothing's worked."

His eyebrows raised. "Really?"

I nodded. "I know you might not believe me, but it's true. I don't know what else to do anymore."

He took a sober breath. Then, he spoke. "Feisal, I wish I could do more for you. At this stage, all I can provide is some advice. Would you like that?"

I liked this doctor. I liked that he asked me for my input instead of just jumping into a tangent.

"Yes, please," I said.

Dr. Jenson cleared his throat. "The thing is, you must remember that some people are very unhappy with their lives. I'm not saying that this is your parents, exactly-," he gave me a look as if to let me know that my parents were, in fact, the kind people that he was talking about, "-however, these unhappy people often try to make other's lives miserable. From my experience in counseling, parents do this sort of thing all the time."

I nodded, accepting this. It was one of the first helpful things I'd ever been told about my situation.

"I understand that it's hard for you to get help. We'll do everything that we can to set you up for success here. But regardless, you'll need to be strong. Pray about it and hang in there as long as you can. I promise it'll get better."

At my incredulous look, he added, "Really, it will. Once you turn eighteen, your life will be in your hands. You can leave and never turn back if that's what you choose to do."

Something in his eyes told me that he was speaking not just out of kindness, but perhaps out of personal experience as well.

After the initial intake interview, Dr. Jenson took me up the elevator to the floor that I would be staying on. I expected this facility to be like the last one—for the doors to open up to a world of chaos.

But when the doors peeled back to let us out, I was surprised. There were no screaming kids or staff members. Nobody was running around or throwing things. It was totally quiet. Dr. Jenson led me to my room. He gave me a small plastic bucket of hygiene products. I was about to walk into my room, but he stopped me with a hand on my shoulder.

"Feisal, don't ever tell anybody why you're here. Don't tell anybody any of your business. People are not always kind. They will use your words against you. I can't promise you much, but I can promise you that."

I swallowed thickly. Then, I thanked him and walked into my room.

Another big difference between this facility and the one that I'd gone to previously was that at this facility, I had a roommate.

My roommate was a kid a few years older than me, named Jack. He was a white kid, but he seemed to come from a rough background. His entire wardrobe consisted of camo-print. Camo-print shirts, camo-print pants, camo-print ballcaps. Hell, I wouldn't be shocked if it turned out that his underwear was camo-print.

As soon as he saw me, he brusquely asked, "Who the hell are you?"

"Feisal," I answered politely, settling down on my bed.

"Jack," he introduced himself. "What're you in for?"

I opened my mouth to speak, but then I remembered Dr. Jenson's words. I took a moment to think of something convincingly dismissive.

I didn't have to worry about it. By the time I'd gotten up the nerve to talk again, Jack had already lost interest in the conversation.

At first, I didn't think Jack was the worst roommate. He was mostly polite and usually quiet. Sometimes he engaged in small talk with me. Usually, though, we just coexisted. I eventually learned that he was there because he was fighting with his brother a lot and had been flunking out of school.

"It's because of the principal, man. Guy's got it out for me," Jack said once, shaking his head. "So, yeah, I got into a few fights with him. And my algebra teacher. But that's only because she's kind of a bitch about homework."

Jack's favorite thing to talk about, though, was his escape plan. I don't know why, but he was dead set on breaking out of the facility.

Every time he would start going on about some elaborate escape scheme, I'd just sit there, internally rolling my eyes.

Boy, how in the hell do you plan on doing all that? This place is locked up, I'd think. But I never contradicted what he was saying. I'd just listen and nod. Every so often, I'd bring something up that he hadn't thought of, like the fact that the windows on every floor except for the first were permanently locked, and he'd go quiet for a moment while he thought of a way around this unexpected obstacle.

Eventually, Jack and I got pretty damn close. I'd go as far as to say that we were friends.

I even disregarded Dr. Jenson's words and told Jack about the reason I was in the facility to begin with.

After I told him everything, he sighed.

"Man, that sucks," Jack said. I could tell that he wanted to say something more empathetic, but he just didn't have the right vocabulary. "My uncle's a cop. He could help you if you wanted."

We were lying in our beds, turned towards each other. It had become our ritual to talk for an hour or so after lights out.

I shrugged. "You can tell your uncle. But I don't want my dad to go to jail or anything. I just want to get out of there."

"I guess."

It was then that I noticed how intensely Jack was staring at me. His eyes were round and unblinking. I felt a shiver go down my spine. It looked like he wanted to kill me or something.

Did I say something wrong? I wondered. Maybe I'd insulted him by telling him that I didn't want his cop uncle to arrest my dad.

Either way, something about his gaze was making me too uneasy to go to sleep. I squinted my eyes shut, cracking them just enough to keep watch over him. I expected him to turn over and go to bed after he realized that I was done talking. But he didn't. He just kept staring. After a few minutes of silence, he spoke.

"You asleep, Feisal?"

Should I just pretend to be asleep?

I shook my head. "Not yet."

"Okay. I was just wondering."

Okay. Maybe he was just zoning out.

"Do you want to try something?" His tone had gotten darker. My entire body tensed. My heartbeat picked up.

"What?"

"Just come here."

He stood up and out of bed. Then, he tiptoed over to our door. We were allowed to have it cracked at night, but we were never allowed to close it all the way. Jack glanced out the door, then when the coast was apparently clear, he waved me over.

Oh, God. He's finally going to do it. He's going to bust out of here. And he wants to take me with him!

Still, curious and trusting as I was, I complied. I walked over to him. As I did, he seemed to get more and more antsy.

"Okay, I'm over here. Now what do you want?" I hissed.

Jack stared at me for a long time. Then, in one swift motion, he bent down and removed his pants and underwear.

I'd almost completely forgotten all about Benny.

Back when we lived in the Virginia house, during Mom's decline (but a few months before her death), there was this family friend who stayed with us. His name was Joe. We knew him from church. We relied on him pretty heavily during the initial stages of Mom's edema to help with her daily care.

Joe didn't come alone, though. He had a teenage son, Benny. Benny stayed with us as well. Benny typically slept on the couch. But one night, he came into my bed to sleep with me.

He slipped into my bed with a natural ease, as if he belonged there. The movement shook me awake.

Who the hell is that?

He wrapped an arm around me. I could feel his breath against my neck. His shoulders and chest rose and fell against my back. Eventually, I got enough of my bearings to realize who it was.

"Benny? Hey, what-,"

Benny put his hand over my lips to quiet me.

I don't remember falling asleep. But I must have. Because the next thing I knew, I was waking up to my pants and underwear down around my ankles, and my penis inside of Benny's mouth.

I didn't know how to react. I started to squirm. As I tried to reach for my underwear, Benny grabbed my wrist and pinned my hand down.

"Benny, stop it!" I hissed. I don't know why I kept my voice down. Was I trying to keep Benny from getting in trouble? Maybe I was worried that if he were caught, *I'd* somehow get in trouble too. "Benny. Benny, come on."

Benny didn't acknowledge my distress. He just kept going.

Embarrassment and helplessness filled me. I hardly even had a name for what was happening, but I knew that it was messed up. And I was ashamed that I'd let it happen to me.

I'm so stupid! How could I have fallen asleep?

I tried to call out for help, but I just couldn't. My voice wouldn't work. So, I gave up. I lay there until it was over.

Afterward, Benny let my arms go and helped me pull up my underwear and pants. He looked at me with a smile, as if I was supposed to have liked it. I felt sick to my stomach.

As time went on, Benny didn't stop. Once he'd gotten away with it, he was confident in his ability to *continue* getting away with it. This changed me. I began acting up—lashing out against my teachers, my friends, and even my family. I picked fights with other kids just to prove to myself that I wasn't as weak as Benny made me feel every night.

I was a nightmare. I terrorized my poor sister. I'd destroy her dolls and hide them around the house. I even threw a live crab at her. It sounds ridiculous—but it's true. She still has a scar from where it pinched her with its claws.

I never said anything about what Benny was doing to me, even though Benny never told me to keep what was happening between us a secret. My shame kept me silent. It clogged my throat, twisted my tongue, and forced me into silence.

Eventually, it seemed that the nights spent in my bed were not enough for Benny. He began grabbing me whenever he could, sometimes even pulling me into an empty room.

The last time he did it, he'd yanked me into the bathroom. He closed the door behind me before swiftly stripping my clothes off of me. Terror lanced through my body. The entire ordeal seemed so much *realer* under the harsh bathroom lights.

I was used to Benny sneaking into my room late at night. I was used to not having to face him. Not having to look into his eyes.

Claustrophobia consumed me, and I felt the urge to rip myself out of my own skin.

"I don't want to get in trouble," I whisper-snapped.

Benny didn't say anything. He just lifted me up. Benny shifted me around awkwardly. At first, I didn't know what he was doing. It took me a second to realize that he was trying to penetrate me.

I couldn't collect my bearings fast enough. Benny lowered me down. And like that, he had entered me.

The agony of that moment was indescribably awful. I felt torn apart, both physically and emotionally. My body hurt. I felt disgusting. For the first time since Benny had started touching me, I cried. Benny moved a little, but that just made me cry louder.

This must've made him nervous because he let go of me. I managed to wriggle out of his grip. My backside burned, and when I put a hand there to inspect it, I felt something wet. I was *bleeding.*

Benny tried to touch me again, this time on the face. But I wasn't having it anymore. I shoved him away, grabbing my clothes and putting them back on.

"Feisal-,"

"Leave me alone!" I said sternly.

Benny covered my mouth with his hand. "Shh! Shut up!"

But I'd had enough. I bit down on his hand as hard as I could, and he was forced to release me. We wrestled for a bit in the bathroom. Benny was bigger and older than me, but I compensated for the difference by fighting dirty. I pinched the underside of his arm and used my nails to scratch him. I kicked him in the groin. I bit.

I managed to fight my way out of the bathroom. Stumbling, I made my way down the stairs. I knew that Joe was sleeping on the couch down there.

Benny followed after me. He stopped dead in his tracks when he saw me hovering over Joe's sleeping form. I could see it in his eyes—he was begging me not to wake up his dad.

I stared at Benny long enough to warn him that I *just might* wake Joe. Then, I shoved past him and marched right back up the stairs. I closed the door and locked it. A rush of exhilaration filled me.

I'd done it. I'd finally fought back.

Back in the present, I shook my head at Jack. His pants were still around his ankles. But I wasn't going to let him pressure me into whatever sick game he wanted to play.

"Hell no, man. Don't do that to me ever again," I snapped. Then, I marched back to my bed.

Jack, embarrassed by his actions and my rejection, went back to his own bunk.

As I drifted to sleep, I couldn't help but think of my situation with Benny years ago. I'd almost completely forgotten about what he'd done to me. Jack had reopened the floodgates to a memory I'd long suppressed.

I felt betrayed by Jack and Benny. I felt proud of myself for fighting back. I felt dirty from my own loss of innocence.

Yet, the more I thought about it, the more I began to feel a different emotion: resentment.

Dad had known Joe and Benny. He hadn't been close with either of them—but he'd been familiar enough with them to dislike Benny.

Benny was the kind of kid that Dad disdainfully referred to as a *"punk."* He got in trouble with the police, he ran with gangs, and he was just a little *off.* Even though Dad had long distanced himself from all of us at that point, he was still aware of Joe and Benny's presence in the house.

And he'd done nothing to protect me from Benny.

I'd always thought that there had been a sudden and dramatic shift in my father's behavior. For the past year, I'd carried two mental schemas for him; one of the man that he was in my childhood, and one of the man that he was now. In the former, I'd remembered Dad as a loving and protective father.

But maybe I'd been wrong all along. Maybe Dad hadn't changed. Maybe he'd always been terrible.

After all, he'd been so absent during my upbringing that he'd done nothing to stop me from being sexually abused on a nightly basis for months. He'd left me to fend for myself. Mom couldn't save me. She was sick. And my siblings were too young to understand what was going on. That just left him.

And when it all came down to it, he hadn't been there.

The next day, I spoke to one of the counselors about my rooming situation. They promptly had me moved to a different room, away from Jack. Despite this, Jack didn't seem to hold any ill will toward me. He even made it a point to say goodbye to me the day before his discharge.

With him gone, I was back to being alone in the facility.

But that was fine. After all, I'd practically been alone for all my life leading up to this point anyway. What was another few weeks on my own? I could handle that, easy.

Chapter 29

APPLE IN THE BASEMENT

I didn't color at this facility nearly as much as I did at the other one. I didn't want to deal with the staff taking away my coloring pages again. And I knew that they would—the staff at this facility were far stricter. They weren't mean. They just ran a tighter ship.

Other than the atmosphere, though, this facility wasn't much different than the other one. I still went to group sessions and doctor's appointments. And I still dreaded my discharge day, which was starting to creep closer at an alarming rate.

I'd already gone home once.

This facility had a "leave" policy. Kids were sent home for a few hours a week or two before discharge to ensure a "successful re-acclamation." I didn't want to go home before I absolutely had to, but policy was policy.

I went in expecting the worst. But what I saw floored me.

My brother was nowhere to be found when I walked into the house. He wasn't in the den, nor was he in our bedroom. Dad hadn't mentioned him visiting a friend's house. Which meant that there was only one other place where he could be: the basement.

After the success of my laundry room punishment, Dad and Kalisha had taken to locking Wayne in the dark basement without food or water whenever they wanted to set him straight. It was cruel and I hated it. But there was nothing I could do.

I saw Wayne only once during that visit. He'd knocked on the door to use the restroom, and Dad had graciously allowed him to go to the bathroom. My eyes watered when I saw him. I'd only been at the facility for a few weeks, but Wayne had lost so much weight in that short period of time that he practically looked like a skeleton. His elbows and knees were knobby, bones straining against tightly wrapped skin. His face looked like someone had sucked all of the oxygen out of him.

After he'd finished in the bathroom, Dad escorted him back to the basement. He gave Wayne a single apple before locking the door behind him.

Then, Dad joined Kalisha, Cal, Maya, and me in the den. We watched a movie as if my brother weren't being starved alive right below us. It made me sick to my stomach. I felt guilty for leaving my brother alone with my dad, but I knew that if I hadn't gone to the facility, I'd just be starving right along with him.

Close to the end of my stay, I met with my therapist to discuss my return home. For obvious reasons, it wasn't the most fun conversation for me to be having.

My therapist at this facility was a white woman in her 40s. She had brown, chin-length hair and exclusively wore frumpy brown cardigans. The therapy room itself was right in the middle of the floor, and I always felt like everyone else could hear us through the thin walls.

When we spoke, I always used a quieter tone. The therapist didn't seem to have the same reservations about privacy as I did, however, and would usually restate exactly what I'd just said in a louder voice—as if she was *trying* to let everyone else in on what we were discussing.

"So, how are you doing today, Feisal? Is everyone still treating you well here?"

"I'm doing well. And yes, they are," I said automatically. This was my third formal session with her since coming to the facility. And my answer to those two introductory questions had not changed once.

This therapist had a knack for covering old ground. During our sessions, we talked extensively about *anger.* I had anger—I'm not denying that. But I liked to think that the level of anger I possessed was not odd for a kid suffering under my conditions.

We talked a little bit about my abuse at home. But whenever we talked about it, my therapist was much more concerned over my "histrionics" in *reporting* the abuse over the actual abuse itself. Every time I tried to broach the topic of my father's beatings or Kalisha's manipulation, my therapist would just cock her head and say some dumb platitude before switching the topic back to my alleged anger issues, like, *"It must be difficult to feel like these things are happening. But that's why I'd like for you to work on your anger. If you do, I'm sure you'll see less overall conflict in the home. Don't you?"*

It was clear that she wasn't taking my story seriously.

My therapist tapped her notebook with the butt-end of her pen. "Now, it looks like your discharge date is coming up very soon. How do we feel about that?"

"Not great," I said brusquely. "I mean, what's going to happen? Am I just going to have to go back to that house after everything I've been through in there?"

"I don't think I understand what you mean," she said dryly. Good lord, I wanted to grab her head and shake some sense into her.

"Seriously? After everything I've told you, you're just going to force me to go back there?" I asked, incredulous. I usually wasn't so argumentative with my counselors, but this woman had gotten on my last nerve. She didn't offer me a shred of sincerity or empathy. She had prescribed me a narrative on our first meeting, and she was determined to stick with it despite everything I had told her. I'd had enough. "Well, if you guys aren't going to help me, you might as well just send me back home now."

"Feisal," she said. Her tone was sharper than usual. It was as though she'd been momentarily possessed by the ghost of someone who actually knew how to do their damn job. "I *have* listened to what you've said over our previous sessions. I'm not being purposefully obdurate."

"Oh, really?"

"It's not that I'm not hearing what you're saying. It's that I simply don't believe that you're telling me the whole truth."

This caught me completely off-guard. "What?" my voice cracked a little.

"Well, you're very quick to talk about this *abuse*, which I find highly unusual. When children are abused, they rarely want to talk about it. Frankly, your openness is contradictory to what you've been telling me."

Bitch, what? I couldn't believe my ears. This woman had been listening to me the whole time. She'd heard my story. And she'd decided that simply because I was talking about the horrible things that had happened to me, those horrible things couldn't possibly exist.

I rose out of my chair, fury pulling me to my feet. "You've got to be kidding me. Lady, I talk about the abuse because I'm trying to get some help. How the hell is anyone supposed to help me if I don't talk about it?"

How the hell is anyone supposed to help me if I do? I thought, miserable.

I didn't wait for her response. I just stormed out.

244

Once again, I was taken for a fool. Once again, I had gone unbelieved. I felt frustrated and stupid.

But at least now I finally knew why nobody had ever helped me. They all must've thought that I was just a troublemaking liar. An attention-seeking brat.

Apparently, I had not learned proper decorum for disclosing my abuse to others.

After I got back to my room, one of the staff came by to tell me that my discharge date had been moved up. I was going to go home that weekend. She smiled as she broke the news as if it was some great thing that my stay at the facility was being cut short.

I didn't say anything.

I just nodded in pure and utter defeat.

Chapter 30

MUSIC TO MY EARS

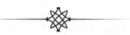

Things did look up for a few weeks after I left the facility.

Mostly because Dad decided that he and Kalisha needed to split up. Apparently, their fighting had escalated to an even worse degree while I was in treatment. Dad had decided that the relationship was unsalvageable, and as soon as I got home, he told me to pack up my things because we were moving out. The news that Dad was breaking up with Kalisha was music to my ears.

I still blamed Kalisha for Dad's behavior. I felt that if she were taken out of the equation, I might still have a shot at repairing my broken relationship with him. Hell, maybe he'd even start acting like my *dad* again.

Anyway, Wayne and I didn't waste a second packing our things. We ran like roaches do when you turn on the lights. We wanted to hurry before Dad had a chance to change his mind.

As soon as we were packed, Dad took us away in his truck. He explained to us on the drive to our new place that he and Kalisha would likely be separating. He even half-apologized for the way he'd been treating us lately.

"I know y'all don't like living there," Dad said, shaking his head. "Anyways, I don't know for sure what's going to happen yet, but this is how it'll be for the time being."

I nodded, taking all of this in. On one hand, I was cautiously optimistic. Without Kalisha, there was nobody around to encourage Dad to beat on us. Nobody to stop us from eating meals. Nobody to turn us against each other.

But on the other hand, this was *exactly* the reason that I worried. Because what if this situation turned out to be worse? What if Kalisha wasn't the thing causing Dad to beat on us?

My mind flickered back to the night that Dad had almost killed me. Kalisha had been the one to pull him away. In this new living arrangement, there would be nobody around to stop Dad from taking punishments too far.

And that thought scared the daylights out of me.

The apartment that we moved into was small but clean. Within days, it was evident that Dad was taking the separation very poorly. He talked about Kalisha constantly, always finding new ways to bring her up in every conversation. He mentioned Cal and Maya all the time, bringing up stories from before my siblings and I had even moved in with them.

Wayne and I were rightfully annoyed. We thought that Dad would forget about Kalisha, Cal, and Maya. We thought he'd been stoic—maybe even a little self-righteous—about the break-up, like he had been with Mom when their relationship had fizzled out. But that wasn't the case. Dad missed Kalisha's family, and he was trying to get us to miss them, too.

It hit me that Dad actually *did* love those people. Maybe even more than he'd ever loved Mom or us. I had to wonder if Dad had ever moped around Kalisha's house like this before we'd moved in with him. If he'd ever talked about our old stories.

I highly doubted it.

Regardless, I didn't want to complain too much. Things *were* markedly better without Kalisha and her kids around.

Dad was still strict, but he wasn't nearly as hotheaded or paranoid as before. He let Wayne and I go outside to play. We watched movies together in the living room (always some disturbing rated-R flick that Dad had no business showing us). We were even allowed to laugh and make jokes. It was surreal. For the first time in forever, I was finally beginning to see the father from my memories resurfacing.

Dad seemed lighter during this period of time. He played pranks on Wayne and me often, sometimes popping out of corners to scare us just like Mom used to do at our house in Virginia.

248

Other times, he just talked with us. I remember one time; Dad and I were sitting on the stoop in front of the apartment building. It was a nice day, and we both wanted some fresh air. We'd been talking about the recent college basketball games that had been playing on TV until we'd hit a lull in our conversation.

Dad sighed. "Hey, you want to go back, right?"

"Huh?" I asked.

"To the other house? To be with Kalisha and Cal and Maya?"

I didn't know how to answer. Deep down, I wanted to scream *No!* and have that be the end of it. But I knew that Dad was miserable without Kalisha. And I also knew that if I said *no,* Dad would probably get angry with me. But I didn't want to say *yes,* either. Lying to Dad didn't sit right with me.

So, I just shrugged.

I'd had a stirring feeling in my gut lately that something bad was going to happen. This conversation with Dad seemed to confirm it. Before the next words were out of his mouth, I already knew what he was going to say.

We were moving back into the Chester Street house.

That night, Wayne and I conspired in our room.

Neither of us wanted to go back to the old house. We were well aware of the world that Dad was taking us back into, and both of us partly resented him for it. If only he'd been stronger. If only he wasn't so dependent on Kalisha's love. If that were the case, maybe he could have moved on.

Wayne and I tried not to dwell on these hypotheticals. We'd more than learned at this point that thinking up *what-ifs* only ever served to make us more miserable in the long run.

The only thing that we could do—the only thing that we knew *how* to do at this point—was to continue surviving. To move forward.

"What do we do?" Wayne eventually asked.

I shrugged. "What can we do? Not much, other than hope that Kalisha and her kids will take some mercy on us for once." I had to laugh. Hell would freeze over before that woman ever took pity on us.

"We can run away," Wayne suggested timidly.

I raised a brow. "We?"

He looked me dead in the eyes, and I understood. Wayne was tired of being left behind. He didn't want to watch me make my grand escapes anymore. He wanted to be taken with me. At once, I felt a determined fire ignite in my gut.

I knew from all my failures that the chances of Wayne and I successfully running away were slim. But each time I'd tried, I'd gotten a little further. And that had to stand for something. Maybe with my brother with me, I'd be able to go the full distance.

Maybe this time would be different.

"If it gets bad, we will," I said. I exhaled, settling into my blankets. Knowing that our time in the apartment was running out, I tried my best to enjoy the comfort of my bed. It would be a long time before I enjoyed this kind of comfort again.

Chapter 31

TWO IS BETTER THAN ONE

Surprisingly, things did not go south immediately once we moved back into the Chester Street house. It seemed the time and space apart had reformed Kalisha and her kids. For about a month, things were calm. At least, as calm as they had ever been. Wayne and I were fed properly, we got along with Cal and Maya, and nobody was beaten any bloodier than they had to be.

It was nice, but it also made me a little bitter.

Now, why was this so hard? If it's like this now, doesn't that mean it could've always been like this?

Of course, the peace didn't last long.

By the end of our honeymoon period of return, things had gone right back to normal.

Which meant one thing for Wayne and me: that it was time to leave.

The rain came down in sheets, cold water pummeling the ground. By all accounts, it was not an ideal day to run away from home. But Wayne and I didn't care. We were on a mission.

Taking a note out of Jack's book, I'd planned this escape in a bit more depth. This time, I had a mission in mind. I was going to take Wayne, and we were going to go back to Virginia. Once we were there, we'd find our way to Aunt Nina's. We'd convince her to keep us.

The fastest way to Virginia was by plane. So, Wayne and I were currently racing like our lives depended on it to the airport.

We'd been running for hours. *Brutal* was one way to describe our journey thus far. We were cold, soaking wet, and tired. After about two hours of nonstop jogging, we'd started to pace ourselves a little, walking for a mile or two before picking up our jog again.

Neither of us had eaten or drank anything.

"I'm going to pass out," Wayne hissed. He didn't look good at all. I wasn't faring much better.

I patted his shoulder. "We'll find some food," I promised.

I looked around vigilantly and spotted a gas station. I nodded my head toward it, gesturing for Wayne to follow me.

The gas station was freezing cold when we walked in. They were pumping their air conditioning at an unholy intensity. Wayne and I shivered as we walked to the back of the store to grab some snacks. We picked out a few bags of pretzels and chips and a large drink to share. Then, we took it up to the register. Wayne let me do the talking.

The guy at the register gave us a look. I didn't blame him. We were so sopping wet; we'd left a trail of water behind us in the store.

He rang up the snacks and drink. "That'll be four seventy-nine."

I felt my chest squeeze a little. "Well, sir, the thing is— we don't have any way to pay for it."

"Sorry?"

"I don't have any money. Is there any way I can buy this stuff without paying? Please, my brother and I are starving."

"Can't your parents buy it for you?"

"No."

"Why not?"

"They don't know we're here," I said. At his perplexed expression, I slowly explained, "My Dad and his girlfriend aren't very good people. They... beat us." I tried being a little more reserved with my disclosure, remembering how I hadn't been believed previously due to my lack of hesitation.

The guy assessed me for a moment. Then, he held up a hand. "Hang on. I'll be right back."

He walked to the back of the store. I couldn't see him from where I was, but I could hear that he was on the phone.

This wasn't good news. I grabbed Wayne by the arm and raced out of the store. Wayne recognized my urgency and ran along with me without question.

My guess was that this guy had just called the cops. And since I didn't exactly have the best track record with the police at this point, I knew that as soon as they arrived on the scene, they'd be carting Wayne and me right back home.

There was a chance that the guy was trying to help us. But I couldn't take the gamble. I'd been burned too many times by blindly trusting others. I wasn't going to make that mistake again.

Wayne and I kept hearing sirens. I assumed that it was the police looking for us. I told Wayne to stop running. Running would only make us look more suspicious. There was a main route to the airport but going that way would take us straight through a busy street. Given that I was already a little edgy from our interaction at the convenience store, I wasn't eager to go that way. Instead, I took Wayne down a more winding path, through a field behind a main row of houses.

Walking in the field was miserable. We kept tripping on roots and falling on puddles. But it did offer us one thing: a shed. There was an open shed at the back of someone's property, and Wayne and I took the initiative to hide in there for a little while until the worst of the weather subsided.

In the shed, we found a lot of clothes. I'd never stolen a thing in my life before, but we were so soaked through that I couldn't stop myself. I put on a too-big jacket and a pair of sweatpants. Wayne swapped into a matching set.

The dry clothes gave us a little more energy.

And soon, the storm had subsided enough for us to push on.

I sent a silent prayer up to the heavens, thanking God for having my back.

We continued our trek to the airport. And soon, we saw something that gave us hope. Airplanes. From where we were in the field, we could see the airplanes taking off down the runway, one after the other.

Even though this was my most planned out escape attempt yet, I was still a child with a warped sense of how the world worked. I didn't realize that there was no way in Hell someone would let my brother and I board a plane with no tickets, luggage, or parental permission.

Still, the airport seemed like a divine gift.

Wayne and I didn't want to go in through the front of the airport. There were too many people there. And besides, wouldn't officers be stationed at the doors? Instead, we climbed the fence near the back and found a door leading in.

We knocked on the door, and a young-looking employee pulled us into the building. He looked shocked to see us and didn't hold himself back from bombarding us with questions.

"What are you doing here? How did you get to the back door? Where are your parents?"

I explained to the man that my brother and I wanted to be flown to Virginia to be with our family. This needed to happen, I said, because my dad and his girlfriend were mistreating us terribly—and the only way for us to escape the abuse was to leave the state.

The employee looked at me incredulously. Wayne grabbed my arm, unsure. I realized that I was blowing this. I needed to keep talking. I needed to convince him somehow that I was telling the truth.

I went into detail about what went on at home. I talked about the individual cruelties both my brother and I had endured. Wayne, though less eager to speak, backed me up. Eventually, I couldn't take it anymore, and I started to cry.

This must've made something in the guy's brain click. He nodded stiffly, "I'll try my best to help you out. I don't know if we can fly you two to Virginia without a ticket, but maybe there's another way we can be of assistance. Come on, we can go to my office."

He took us to his office and sat us at his desk. He brought us snacks and water, and for a while, we just ate and talked.

After an hour or so, I began to relax. It was clear that this guy truly believed our story and wanted to help. I almost let myself believe that he would.

But then a knock came at the door, and two women walked in.

My heart sank to the pit of my gut. I knew exactly who these women were: Tall and Short, the DHS agents who had taken me home once before. I bristled.

"Hi, Feisal," Short said, her voice honey-sweet, "I see you still haven't learned your lesson yet. Well, I guess we'll just have to take you to jail then."

The airport employee straightened up. "You're going to help him, right?" he asked.

Short nodded, but I spoke before she could. "They're not going to help us," I said. "They never do. They're just going to take me right back home, like they've done before."

Tall interrupted me. "Thank you for all your help, sir. We'll make sure these two are taken care of."

As we were forced out of the guy's office, I could see the regret on his face. I could see him thinking, *what did I just do?*

I tried my best to forgive him. He couldn't have known.

Wayne and I were taken to the DHS office immediately. Like before, we were forced to sit in a cubicle while our case files were processed. The entire time, Short and Tall kept taunting us, telling us that we were going to jail. I snapped right back every time that I welcomed jail. Jail would be paradise compared to home.

"So, why'd you run away from home this time?" Tall asked. "And why'd you drag your brother into it?"

I tried to tell them about everything that had happened since our last encounter. The new horrors that both of us had been forced to endure.

But Short just shook her head and said, "You ought to feel bad for putting your parents through this shit all of the time. Hell, if you were my kid, I'd beat you, too. Teach your ass how to act."

"It's ingratitude," Tall added. "You've got parents who love you, who worry about you. And all you care about is yourself. Do you know what would happen to you if you were taken into the system? You'd be sent to a house much, much worse than yours."

I snorted. I highly doubted that a house worse than mine even existed.

At the end of the day, we were taken back to the Chester Street house. And like that, the last of my hope was finally extinguished.

Chapter 32

BARE SKIN

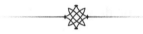

The beatings only got worse from there. This was the point that my abuse reached its peak.

One day, Dad came home after being gone for the weekend. He was already in a bad mood when he walked through the door. I could already tell that I was in for it. These days, Dad barely needed an excuse to beat the crap out of me.

He stormed into his bedroom. I heard things shuffling around. Dad was looking for something, and his search was clearly hopeless.

From the living room, I could hear Dad begin to go at it with Kalisha. They weren't yelling at each other any louder or more intensely than usual, but I could feel an undercurrent of tension in the atmosphere.

I was almost stupid enough to believe that the storm might be contained between them. But then, Dad threw open the door of his room. He came out madder than a raging bull, yelling at the top of his lungs. He demanded to know which one of us had been going through his stuff.

Of course, none of us were at fault. Everyone in the house knew not to go into Dad and Kalisha's room without permission.

Dad found us in the living room. His entire body was tensed, every muscle in his jaw flexing. "Who did it?" he demanded to know.

I looked between Wayne and Cal. Both of them had the same blank expression on their faces that I did. Usually, when stuff like this went down, I suspected Cal. It wasn't exactly below him to look for ways to get Wayne and me in trouble.

But looking at him now, I could already tell that he was as genuinely innocent as any of us were.

"Y'all conspiring with each other?" Dad asked, noticing how we were looking at one another.

"No," I said. "We're just confused-,"

"Don't start running your mouth, Feisal. It was probably you," Dad growled.

"Dad, I swear, I didn't."

"Oh, don't start." Dad's voice came out vicious. "I fucking know it was you. Now, come over here."

His hand shot out, and he grabbed me by the shirt. He pulled me into his room, slamming the door shut behind me. Kalisha was sitting on the bed, looking utterly bored. I tried to look at her in a silent plea for help, but she just rolled her eyes at me.

"Strip down, Feisal," Dad snapped.

I looked at him as if he'd grown a second head.

He smacked me hard on the back. I wheezed.

"I'm not telling you again."

Gritting my teeth, I did as told. I stripped down until I was bare. Humiliation burned through my body. But this emotional pain was just a small precursor for the real damage that was to come. Dad pulled his thick belt from his trousers and told me to turn around. Then, he began to whip me with it.

At first, his hits were accurate—always landing squarely on my backside. But then, they grew more erratic. He hit me everywhere: my butt, my legs, my back, my thighs, my groin, and my stomach. Only my face was spared, and that was probably because it was the only part of me that couldn't be hidden behind a layer of clothes.

Sometimes when Dad beat me, I could get used to the repetition of it. His fists always hurt, but he'd fall into a rhythm with them—and that made it easier for me to brace between every hit. I couldn't get used to the belt, though.

Each crack of Dad's belt ignited a fire in my body. My flesh felt like it was being ripped apart. He beat me so hard that reddish welts began to form instantly as soon as the leather made contact with my skin.

I tried to protect myself—at one point reaching to snatch the belt out of my father's hand. But this only emboldened Dad.

If I was smart, I would've just laid there. I would've collapsed onto the floor, and I would've let Dad stomp on my face and kill me. It would be an easier punishment than enduring, enduring, enduring.

But I was always a fighter. And it wasn't in my nature to stand down. So, I struggled. And the more I struggled, the longer the punishment lasted.

Dad cracked the belt against my legs, and the thin side of the leather caught me. I couldn't bear the pain. I crumpled to my knees. My vision was starting to go hazy. Black fuzz edged my eyesight. Instinctively, I knew that Kalisha wasn't coming around to help me this time. If I didn't do something soon, I'd pass out.

And if that happened, it would be a toss-up on whether or not Dad would keep going.

Fearing for my life, I gritted my teeth and scrambled for the door. It took Dad a second to realize that I was slipping away. When he did, he started to chase after me. But I'd managed to beat him out the door.

I ran to my room, throwing myself under my blankets. It was a feeble defense. Dad could've grabbed me and dragged me right back to his room.

But he didn't. He just cursed at me from the hallway for a few seconds, as if the doorway to my room had some kind of protective force field built into it. Then, Dad retreated back to his room and slammed the door shut.

I let out a sigh. For now, at least, it was over.

After a few minutes of lying on my bed, I got up. I grabbed a pair of pajama bottoms and staggered to the bathroom to wash myself up.

At first, I didn't even want to look at myself. I showered, averting my eyes from any hint of my own reflection. The warm water soothed as much as it bit, and I didn't even dare try with the soap. I already knew that Dad had broken skin. And from previous beatings, I was aware that putting soap on the wound would only cause it to sting and burn more.

After washing myself, I stepped out of the shower and put on a fresh pair of clothes.

Accidentally, I saw myself in the mirror as I was about to pull my shirt over my head. The instant feeling that consumed me was one of disgust.

My body looked like a scar. My skin was warped and welted and red, and my eyes were hollow with pain. I couldn't stop myself from breaking down. As quietly as I could, I cried.

I'd danced with the idea of dying a few times before. But this time, the thought truly hit me. *I don't want to be alive anymore.* I had no reason to live. My hope of escaping had been dashed with my last and final runaway attempt with Wayne. Even though Dr. Jenson had promised me that things would improve after I turned eighteen, it didn't seem to matter. Why would it, when I was pretty sure that I wouldn't even *live* to see eighteen at this rate?

Suddenly, the bathroom door opened.

Shit! I thought. *I forgot to lock it!*

At first, I panicked, thinking it was Cal or Dad. I quickly pulled my shirt the rest of the way over my body. But it was just Maya.

Maya was still a young kid—even younger than Wayne. She'd never contributed to our punishments like Cal had, but she'd also never tried to stop them from happening. I didn't blame her for that, though. I knew that there was little she could do.

Maya closed the door quietly behind her. Her eyes were wide as she looked at me.

"I heard you crying. Are you okay?" she whisper-asked. I shook my head.

Maya tried to hug me. I told her no, gently pushing her away. "I'm too sore," I said. I gestured down at my body.

Maya reached forward, lifting my shirt to see my body. She cringed at the welts that Dad had left on me. Then, without a word, she grabbed a tub of Vaseline from beneath the bathroom sink and helped me apply the ointment to my stomach, back, and shoulders. I took the jar out of her hand so that I could cover my butt and the back of my legs.

As I applied the Vaseline, Maya began to cry. She held her face in her hands and sobbed, trying (as I did) not to be too noisy about it.

"You have to go, Feisal," Maya said, sniffling. I just stared at her, stunned. "You have to get out of here. They'll keep hurting you if you don't leave. You have to... you have to run away again. But this time, go even farther."

I tried to tell her that I couldn't run away. That I'd tried three times, and every time had ended in failure. But Maya didn't listen. She just kept crying and apologizing. "I'm sorry. I'm so sorry," she kept saying over and over.

"Maya, come on," I said, trying to calm her down. "I wish I could run away. But they'll just send me right back here."

Maya shook her head. "I don't care. You need to try again. You need to keep trying. You can't stay here, Feisal. You can't."

She was right. I couldn't stay.

Even though I knew that running away again would be useless, I promised Maya that I would try.

"And you won't let them take you back here, right?" she asked, wiping her tear-streaked face.

I nodded firmly. "No. I won't."

Chapter 33

NO PERMISSION NEEDED

*I*t's surreal, going to school the day after you're beaten within an inch of your life. Imagine this: your entire body aches, you've got welts and bruises all over, and you're worried that you might not survive to see another day—and then some middle-aged guy tells you that the most important thing in your life should be studying for his trigonometry quiz at the end of the week.

I was so over it that I ended up skipping class.

My friend Kelly found me in the gymnasium after I'd neglected to show up for history.

"What's with you?" she asked. My clothes were long and covered up my injuries. But they couldn't hide the pain in my eyes.

I'd never really talked about my abuse to my friends. On one hand, I was embarrassed about it. On the other, I was afraid that talking about my abuse would peg me as an untrustworthy and histrionic liar in their eyes—just like it did for the DHS officers, the counselors, and the doctors.

Kelly was going through similar things at home, but her situation was a little better. Her dad only beat her when he was drunk.

There was a chance that Kelly wouldn't react well to what I was about to tell her. But I didn't care. I was tired of walling myself off from my friends. I was tired of suffering quietly and alone.

Instead of answering her with words, I pulled up my shirt and showed her my wounds. They looked even worse today than they did when they were fresh.

Kelly gasped, holding her hands to her mouth.

"It's worse in other places," I muttered. I didn't want to freak her out by showing her the more severe marks on my butt and thighs. "I don't know what to do. I think I need to run away again-,"

"No. You can't do that," Kelly insisted. "Listen, Feisal, we need to get you some help."

"I've tried getting help. They all think that I'm just some troublemaking delinquent who's getting what he deserves."

"And you think *running away* will convince them otherwise?" Kelly asked.

I winced. She had a point.

"I don't know what to do. I don't know who can help me at this point," I admitted, feeling pathetically small.

268

Kelly placed a hand on my shoulder. "Just stay here, okay? I'll be right back."

With that, she left.

As promised, she was back shortly. And she hadn't come alone. Following behind her was our history teacher, Mr. Bird, and his assistant, Miss Vera. Mr. Bird and Miss Vera took me back to Mr. Bird's office. Miss Vera politely asked me to show them the marks on my body. *All* of the marks.

I looked at Kelly. She nodded, coaxing me to comply. Trusting her, I did as I was told. I showed Mr. Bird and Miss Vera the bruises and welts—even the ones on my butt and legs. Making myself vulnerable like this felt humiliating. But my spirit was so broken at that point that I could hardly bring myself to care.

I pulled my clothes back on and turned back around. Miss Vera was crying into her hands. Mr. Bird looked pale.

"Feisal," he said, "Kelly talked to me about a facility that you mentioned once to her. Would it be in your best interest to go back to that facility, or another like it?"

"For the short-term, maybe. But it won't help me forever. Every time I get home from one of my facility stays, I get beat worse for talking to the counselors about our *family business,*" I said.

Mr. Bird considered this. "Well, what if we could figure out a long-term plan for you while you were somewhere short-term but safe?"

I shrugged. I didn't know what to say. All of this sounded nice, but I didn't really believe that Mr. Bird of all people could do anything for me. Not when I'd already been failed by everyone else in the world.

Still, there was a spark of determination in his eyes that ignited a little ember of hope in my chest.

"How do you feel right now?" he asked. "Do you feel like hurting yourself or others?"

"No."

"I don't think you understand. Let me rephrase: if you went back to that house, would you hurt yourself?"

I got his drift. "Yes, sir. I would hurt myself."

"Good. Let's go to the principal's office, then. We should have a chat with him."

The next few hours went by in a blur.

Mr. Bird and Miss Vera took me to the principal's office, where I was again asked to show the principal my body. The principal and Mr. Bird talked about some possible solutions—finally settling on the decision that they needed to send me to a safe place immediately.

The principal called my dad to let him know that I would be transferred to a local boy's group home.

Dad was expectedly furious. He tried to insist to the principal that I was full of shit. That I was a compulsive liar, that I'd tried running away from home countless times, and that I was not to be trusted.

"You can't do anything with him without my express permission. I have a right to my son."

The principal's response was simple but solid: "Yes, sir. But I have a duty to my students. if you're terribly concerned, you're free to call the police and have them meet you at the group home after Feisal is brought in."

Then, he hung up.

Then, the principal turned to me. His face was stony. "You need to hurry up now, Feisal. You don't want to be here when your father shows up."

Mr. Bird and Miss Vera helped me pack up my essentials from my locker. Then, Mr. Bird drove me to the boy's group home. When I arrived, the caretakers took pictures of my body and actually asked me about my abuse at home—rather than immediately assuming that I was some kind of deviant with anger issues.

It seemed different. It seemed hopeful.

God, please help me get through this, I prayed. *Let this time be different. I need this time to be different.*

Chapter 34

Boys Group Home

I'd been under the impression that the group home would be just another behavioral facility. Instead, it operated more like a halfway house, providing long-term care for neglected, abused, or troubled teens.

The home offered recreational therapy, regular therapy, a staff of counselors, daily activities, and a lot of other things. But the most exciting part of the home was that they specifically took in clients with long-term stay needs. Unlike the other facilities, which had only kept me for a month at a time at the most, this place would be my home for the next six months.

I stayed in an all-male cottage with a few other boys around my age. The cottage was large, with multiple faculties for whatever we needed. One of the counselors, a young white guy named Brad, showed me around.

To the right of the entrance was a lounge. The lounge featured a few chairs, some wall-corded telephones, and a pool table. A formal rec room branched off from the lounge, fitted with board games, air hockey, ping-pong, and a pinball machine. Further to the right of the cottage was the dining room. To the left was the kitchen.

"Only T-3s and T-4s can go in there, though," Brad said.

Straight ahead was a cozy living room area, with couches and a TV. Behind that were our rooms. Everyone had their own room—each equipped with a bed, a nightstand, a closet, a dresser, and a private bathroom.

The other guys were nice enough. At first, they were skeptical of me. But eventually, I managed to earn their trust.

The staff at the group home also felt a lot more present than they had at the other behavioral facilities I'd been to. There was one woman, Ruby, who was everyone's favorite. She had black hair and wore a great deal of makeup. She kind of reminded me of the main character from the *Hairspray* movie—always upbeat and always kind.

There was another staff member who only met with us on Sundays. His name was Mike, and *weird* only began to describe him.

He was a tall, wiry white guy who exclusively wore Hawaiian shirts and fisherman's pants. His hair was long and curly, and he always wore it in a ponytail. He was also an artist, and not shy about it in the slightest. On his days with us, he'd bring us xeroxed copies of some of his design work, and he'd have us color it.

He was nice but assertive. If he thought we were half-assing our coloring jobs, he would call us out on it.

Sometimes, he'd bring us instruments to play. He never taught us *how* to play the instruments, though, which meant that those afternoons usually gave the rest of the staff a headache from listening to our cacophonic symphony.

Most of the other boys were lukewarm on Mike's antics, but I loved him. He was so weird but so full of life—and I enjoyed every bit of his eccentricities.

Finally, there was my therapist.

Her name was Sheila, and she made all the decisions when it came to my care. I'd been a little wary of Sheila at first due to the experiences I'd had with past counselors, but I quickly learned that she was *nothing* like the other people who had treated me in the past.

Sheila was kind and empathetic. She listened to me when I spoke about my abuse. She smiled often.

And most importantly, she didn't look down on me for talking openly about my trauma. In fact, she encouraged it.

Over our sessions together, I ended up telling Sheila everything. I told her about my childhood. About having to take care of my mom. About being sexually assaulted by Benny. About my dad. About the abuse.

Sheila listened to it all. And she never once made me feel like any of it had been my fault. She promised me that she was working behind the scenes to make sure that I wouldn't have to go back to my father's house after I left the group home.

It was the first time I felt like I'd truly been *listened to.*

And honestly, it made all the difference.

Chapter 35

SHEILA

One big part of the group home's social atmosphere was the *tier system* that it implemented. When new kids moved into the home, they started at the first tier, T-1. As time went on and that kid completed different milestones, they'd be given the option to apply for the next tier.

The main way to successfully apply for the subsequent tier was to collect stars. As in, little yellow star stickers that the staff would put on your chart for doing something positive. Stars could be given for a number of things, such as opening up in therapy sessions or actively participating in an activity. They could also be occasionally earned for especially impressive acts of kindness or leadership, but this was harder to achieve.

Stars weren't exactly easy to get in the first place.

Basically, once a week, the entire treatment team would have a meeting. During this meeting, they'd go down the list of all the kids at the cottage. They'd talk about each kid, dissecting each of his incidents and accomplishments in detail. Then, if the entire team decided that a kid had done his absolute best, they'd grant him a star. We wouldn't know if we'd earned a star until we looked at the starboard on the dining room wall the next day.

If someone had put in an application for a higher tier in the cottage, it would be brought up in the meeting. Anyone could apply whenever they wanted, but if the staff didn't think they were ready, they'd be rejected.

The day after this meeting, Brad would gather all of us to go over the week's activities. He'd bring up any announcements that needed to be made—plans that had been canceled or rescheduled, or messages that needed to be relayed from therapists. Then, he'd go over the "stars of the week."

He'd go down the list of everyone who had applied for a tier upgrade. For example, "Matt applied for tier two, and was sadly denied," or "Matt applied for tier two, and was accepted. Congratulations."

He never went into detail about why someone was denied or accepted in front of all of us, but we could talk to him in private if we had any questions.

This seemed well and good, but tier application rejections were actually quite contentious at the home. There was this one guy, Bobby, who had been a T-2 for quite some time. He'd been gunning for tier three since I'd moved in. When he was rejected, he stood up and snapped, "Are you fucking kidding me? I've worked my ass off, and I'm still not being promoted? This is bullshit."

Brad tried to calm Bobby down, but Bobby wasn't having it. Bobby grabbed his chair and threw it at the door before storming off to his room.

None of us said anything, but we all knew what was going to happen next: if there was ever a situation where someone had to be demoted, staff just had to put in a request and the deed would be done.

The draw of the tier system was that it offered a chance to gain more privileges around the cottage. For example, T-3s and T-4s had access to the kitchens. They could also be given leadership roles during activities.

I climbed the tier system fairly quickly. It wasn't hard— I just had to stay on my best behavior, follow the rules, and give more than half a damn whenever we did activities. Compared to what I was used to at Dad's house, this was a cinch.

By my fourth month, I'd been promoted to T-3. The highest level in the cottage was T-4. I probably could've applied for T-4 without issue, but I wanted to take my sweet time with that final promotion. T-4s got the most incentives, freedoms, and privileges in the cottage. But they were also recommended for discharge sooner. And even though Sheila was working hard to find suitable accommodations for me, she had yet to come up with any real options.

What Sheila *had* managed to do was get in contact with my family in California.

I wasn't close to my Californian relatives, but I didn't dislike them, either. I'd only met them a few times, but they'd seemed like kind and genuine people. Sheila got me in contact with my grandmother, and over the course of a few phone calls and letters, I'd gotten to explain my story to her. My grandmother agreed with Sheila that it would be best for me to move to California.

Unfortunately, it wasn't that easy. According to Sheila, there was a lot of legal stuff that needed to happen if I was ever going to gain freedom from my father.

Finally, during my fifth month at the group home, Sheila came to me with good news: she had talked to a judge and had organized a court date for me to speak to him. This court date, she told me, would offer me the chance to escape my home without repercussion.

I was excited, but I was also nervous. Would the judge believe me? Would he rule in my favor? Authority figures had historically taken my father's word over mine. Why would this be any different?

"Feisal," Sheila said after I'd expressed my anxieties to her, "I know this is scary for you. But I promise, it'll all be okay. This is your chance to speak up about your abuse. It's your chance to get the law on your side."

The crazy thing is—I believed her. Five months ago, I had been totally hopeless and ready to end my own life. And now, I was staring down what might be a new opportunity for a brighter, better future.

I nodded, swallowing down my fear. "Okay," I said. "I'll go."

Chapter 36

THE VERDICT

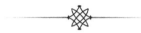

Sheila told me that my dad and Kalisha would meet us at the courthouse. My stomach turned at the thought. I'd practiced delivering my story in my head several times over the past few days, but I worried that my father's presence would mess with my head, causing me to tell it incorrectly.

I knew that I had Sheila and the rest of the group home staff members behind me. But that fact didn't help much to soothe my nerves.

The judge was a Black woman with a stern face.

She's going to take my father's side. I just know it, I thought, miserable.

Even so, I remained hopeful. Sheila had prepared a huge file folder full of documentation regarding my case. She was going to bat for me, and I couldn't be more grateful.

We all settled into the courtroom. As the minutes ticked on leading up to proceedings, I noticed something: Dad was nowhere to be found.

Instead, it was only Kalisha sitting behind the opposing bench. She was wearing casual clothes and had an irate expression—as if being here was some huge inconvenience for her. Sheila informed me in a whisper that she'd just gotten word that my dad wasn't planning to show up at all.

I wasn't sure how to feel. Disappointed? Relieved? Much less unsure of her feelings than I was, the judge didn't seem to approve of Dad's absence at all.

Court began. The judge commanded me to stand before her.

"This is a conversation between you and me," she said, her voice steady. "Please pay no mind to the opposing counsel, regardless of how tempting it may be. When I talk to you, answer my questions with a simple *yes, ma'am,* or *no, ma'am* unless I ask for further elaboration. Do you understand?"

I nodded. "Yes, ma'am."

The judge began asking me a series of questions. She talked mostly to me but occasionally referred to my therapist for more concrete statements. Sheila was adamant about the goodness of my character.

"Feisal has shown amazing progress and success at the home. The other boys look up to him. His behavior is exceptional, and his willingness to participate in both therapy and activities is phenomenal."

I was duly aware of Kalisha rolling her eyes behind me. But as the judge had instructed, I paid her no mind.

"Feisal has expressed wanting a positive relationship with his father," Sheila went on, "but the dynamics between them are unhealthy at best. Feisal's father is abusive, both emotionally and physically. We have had to limit the time that Feisal's father contacts Feisal because his phone conversations with Feisal usually just amount to screaming and belittling. Feisal's father has not attempted to visit Feisal at the home even once. I truly don't see Feisal going back home with his father as an option, your honor."

Sheila went on to present the evidence of my abuse to the court. She talked at length about the stories that I'd told her. And when the judge asked me for my thoughts, I maintained that the stories were true—and that I agreed with Sheila about not returning home.

"We've been in contact with his paternal grandmother, who has been making arrangements for Feisal to stay with some family in California."

"Excuse me," the judge said, cutting Sheila off. "Who said anything about the child moving to California? I've not made that decision yet—and it is *my* decision to make. Not yours."

Sheila deflated a little. "I understand. I apologize for overstepping."

The judge raised a hand to dismiss Sheila. She turned to Kalisha. "Ma'am, you are the girlfriend of the father, yes?"

"That's right," Kalisha said.

"The father's absence shows me how little respect he has for my courtroom, and how little care he has for his child." The judge stated coldly. "If the father is not present at our next court date, I will be removing this child from his custody immediately. The child will be sent to a boy's ranch, and the father will have no access to him. Is this understood?"

Kalisha bristled. This clearly wasn't going her way. To be fair, the judge had thrown *all* of us for a loop with that final declaration.

"Yes, ma'am," Kalisha said.

Then, the judge turned to me. Her voice took on a gentler tone. "Young man, I know things are rough right now. But trust me—things will get better for you. From what I can tell, you are kind and respectful, and you have a bright future ahead of you. If you are unhappy living with your father, I will ensure that you do not have to go back with him. But you need to be sure that this is what you really want. Because once I give my ruling, I will not undo it."

"I understand, ma'am," I said.

In retrospect, I shouldn't have been surprised that my father had chosen not to attend the court proceedings. Dad loved control. More than that, he *needed* it. He must've known that he wouldn't have any control in the courtroom.

It was fine that he hadn't shown up, though. I hadn't needed him. I'd stated my case before the judge, and I'd done it with the support of my care team. I'd even gotten a half-decent verdict.

Leaving the courtroom, I felt lighter than air.

The judge's solution wasn't perfect, and I knew that my troubles were far from over. But to me, her words sounded like hope. They sounded like a *future*.

Better than that, they sounded like a future worth living for.

And to me, a future worth living for was the most beautiful promise in the world.

Printed in the USA
CPSIA information can be obtained
at www.ICGtesting.com
LVHW040356300724
786811LV00004B/403